S0-AJO-722

DATE DUE			

Silverton School Library
1160 Snowden
Box 128
Silverton, CO 81433

PASSAGE TO
LITTLE
BIGHORN

by
TERRY KRETZER-MALVEHY

rising moon
Books for Young Readers from Northland Publishing

FRONTISPIECE:
Sitting Bull photographed by Orlando Scott Goff
Bismarck, Dakota Territory, 1881
Courtesy of the State Historical Society of North Dakota

The author and the publisher give special thanks to
Page Lambert for her insightful consultation.

The cover illustration was rendered in oils on canvas
The text type was set in Weiss
The display type was set in Pabst
Composed and manufactured in the United States of America
Cover designed by Jennifer Schaber
Designed by Sandy Bell
Edited by Heath Lynn Silberfeld
Editorial direction by Aimee Jackson
Production supervised by Lisa Brownfield

Copyright © 1999 by Terry Kretzer-Malvehy
Cover illustration copyright © 1999 by Glenn Harrington
All rights reserved.

This book may not be reproduced in whole or in part, by any means
(with the exception of short quotes for the purpose of review), without
permission of the publisher. For information, address Permissions,
Rising Moon, P. O. Box 1389, Flagstaff, Arizona 86002-1389.

www.northlandpub.com

FIRST IMPRESSION, March 1999
Second Printing, November 1999
ISBN 0-87358-713-8

Library of Congress Cataloging-in-Publication Data

Kretzer-Malvehy, Terry, date.
    Passage to Little Bighorn / Terry Kretzer-Malvehy.
        p.   cm.
    Includes bibliographical references (p.   ).
    Summary: Fifteen-year-old Dakota, who has Lakota blood in him, is
hurled back through time to meet his ancestor Sitting Bull and
witness the massacre at the Battle of Little Bighorn.
    ISBN 0-87358-713-8 (softcover)
    1. Little Bighorn, Battle of the, Mont., 1876—Juvenile fiction.
[1. Little Bighorn, Battle of the, Mont., 1876—Fiction. 2. Time
travel—Fiction. 3. Sitting Bull, 1834?-1890—Fiction. 4. Dakota
Indians—Fiction. 5. Indians of North America—Great Plains—
Fiction.] I. Title.
PZ7.K8845Pas 1999
[Fic]—dc21   98-49481

193/2M/11-99

To the memory of Sitting Bull

AUTHOR'S NOTE

In writing *Passage to Little Bighorn*, I chose to present the story as historical fiction, blending fantasy with history and make-believe characters with real-life heroes. Much current knowledge of Lakota history comes from stories and myths passed down from generation to generation.

SITTING BULL is central among the historical figures of this story's time period. He was known to many as a Hunkpapa chief who flawlessly embodied the Lakota virtues of bravery, generosity, fortitude, and wisdom. He also proved himself to be a man deeply devoted to his family and tribe and one who created unique personal bonds with children, women, and older people—all of whom admired him for his generous nature and kind disposition.

In this story, Dakota Miles is a fictitious character whose mother is Lakota and father is white. The characters related to Dakota—his mother, Savannah; his father, Travis; his grandfather Jon-Jay—and those nineteenth-century characters connected with his Lakota ancestry—Toskala and Tahca Luzahan, along with Peeshkoh and Tahteh—are all fictitious, but through extensive research of Lakota culture and rituals, their personalities and characteristics have been fashioned in the spirit of the Lakota.

Following is a list, in alphabetical order, of other historical characters in this story whose lives left indelible marks on American history.

CAPTAIN FREDERICK BENTEEN Sent by General Custer to lead a battalion to scout along the Wolf Mountains, the captain received an order from the general—

"Come on. Big Village. Be quick. Bring pacs." The orders were soon forgotten when the captain, coming upon Major Reno as he was retreating to higher ground, stopped to aid his friend.

CRAZY HORSE Revered war chief and mystic of the Oglala Sioux, Crazy Horse was instrumental in leading offensive attacks at both the Rosebud and Little Bighorn battles. Only a year after the Little Bighorn battle, Crazy Horse was forced to surrender at the Spotted Tail Agency, where he was killed while resisting arrest.

GENERAL GEORGE CROOK Known to the Lakota as "Three Stars," he led 1,000 soldiers along the Rosebud in his search for Crazy Horse. Instead of success, the general encountered a surprise attack led by the war chief himself.

GENERAL GEORGE ARMSTRONG CUSTER By the age of twenty-three Custer had become the youngest general in the Union army. Years later he was assigned to the Seventh Cavalry with whom he led 210 men against Sitting Bull and his Sioux followers at the Little Bighorn Valley. Known for his impetuous nature and driving ambition, Custer has remained a controversial figure.

FOUR ROBES She was the younger wife of Sitting Bull and the sister of Seen-by-the-Nation.

CAPTAIN GUY HENRY He led a battalion of four companies of the Third Cavalry at the Rosebud battle and was shot by a bullet that went through his left cheek and exited his right cheek. His miraculous recovery resulted only in the loss of sight in his left eye.

MANY HORSES One of four daughters of Sitting Bull, there is little mention of her in historical records. Thus, her character in this story is strictly fictional.

ONE BULL Nephew to Sitting Bull, he took an active part in the fighting at both the Rosebud and the Little Bighorn battles.

PIZI Known to the white man as "Gall," he was the adopted brother of Sitting Bull and the war chief who was instrumental in leading an attack against the Seventh Cavalry. Pizi lost both his wives and three children when the Ree scouts opened fire into the Hunkpapas' tepees.

MAJOR MARCUS RENO He led the attack at the upper end of the Hunkpapa village, losing an estimated one-third of his battalion at what was later named the Reno-Benteen Battlefield.

SEEN-BY-THE-NATION She was the older wife of Sitting Bull and sister of Four Robes.

BATTLE OF THE LITTLE BIGHORN

MAP KEY

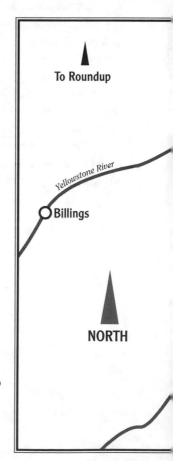

● KEY SITES

1   Last Stand Monument
2   Reno-Benteen Battlefield
3   Battle of the Rosebud
4   Battlefield Road
5   Sitting Bull's Sundance
6   Dakota's capture
7   prehistoric rocks
8   Wolf Mountains
9   Medicine Tail Coulee
10   large black rock

-- ATTACK ROUTES

A   Crazy Horse's attack
B   Custer and his troups
C   Pizi's Attack
D   Reno and Crow scouts
     attack of Sitting Bull's camp

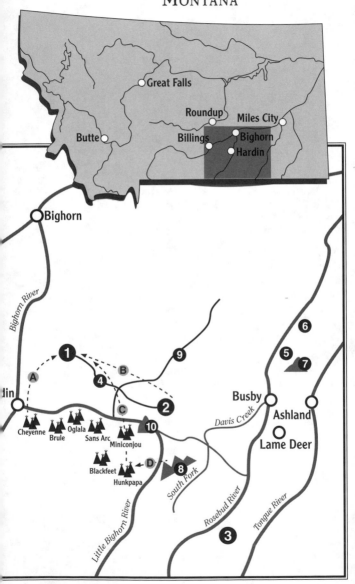

MONTANA

Great Falls

Roundup

Miles City

Butte

Billings   Bighorn

Hardin

Bighorn

Bighorn River

A

1

B

4

9

C

2

Busby

Ashland

Davis Creek

Cheyenne   Oglala   Sans Arc

Brule   Miniconjou

10

Lame Deer

Blackfeet   **D**

Hunkpapa

8

South Fork

Little Bighorn River

Rosebud River

Tongue River

3

din

CHAPTER 1

Battlefield Road

Dakota stared at the grave markers scattered across the lonely hill. Some were in clusters where the soldiers had huddled together in their final moments of terror. "Man-o-man-o-man!" he said, shaking his head in disbelief. How well he could picture the surprise, then the horror, General George Armstrong Custer must have felt when he rounded that last bluff, only to encounter more Indians than anyone could have imagined on that fateful day of June 25, 1876.

Savannah joined her son at the stone wall that surrounded the markers. It was late in the afternoon and most of the tourists had left after the reenactment of the Battle of the Little Bighorn. Flies droned all around them as her words trickled out in a tired voice. "You've got Lakota blood in you, Dakota. You've got to stay close to your family, no matter what happens. Your possessions, your accomplishments—they're nothing, especially if you don't know how to treat others."

Dakota felt his stomach tighten. He tried to imagine life somewhere else, himself a fearless warrior seeking glory and good times, where roosters didn't

wake him up at the crack of dawn, and someone other than an old man greeted him each morning.

Savannah drew closer to her son until their shoulders were touching. Instinctively, Dakota stepped away and gazed across an ocean of pale green and gold shifting in aimless waves under a steel-blue Montana sky. The thought of General Custer leading his men to their deaths, with no chance of escape, shot through him like a bullet, taking his breath away.

Savannah swung around and faced Dakota. "During the time of Sitting Bull and your great great grandfather, Swift Deer, if you stopped caring for your family, then you were no longer considered Lakota."

"Family?" Dakota narrowed his eyes at his mother. The only family he had was a father now living in Alaska with a new wife and baby and Savannah released only a week ago from a therapeutic center for depression in Missoula. He had already wasted two long years in Roundup, living with Jon-Jay, his father's father, a man too old to stop a tottering ranch from crumbling to bits.

Dakota cringed as his mother took his arm and walked him to the end of the parking lot behind the Last Stand Monument. He was glad that the reenactment was finally over. How many times was his mother going to insist he attend this event anyway? Besides, he figured he knew more about the battle than the man standing on the platform. It should have been him telling all those expectant listeners how Sitting Bull had outsmarted the Seventh Cavalry by gathering together more Indians than the general even knew existed. He

smiled again at the recurring vision . . . the general's circle growing smaller and smaller. . . .

At the bottom of the hill Dakota pulled his arm free. "I'm not going by car to the Reno-Benteen Battlefield," he told her, crossing his arms over his chest. "It's seven miles, but I'll be running most of the way."

Savannah inspected her gray cowboy boots, threadbare and weary looking, then scowled at Dakota. "I won't be walking in these," she said, lifting her gaze to the winding road that would eventually end at Reno's Crossing. She hesitated a moment, as if she were measuring the time she would have to visit the museum and browse through the bookstore before Dakota returned to the monument.

"Well," said Savannah, twisting the leather strap on her purse, "we've got until nine o'clock before the grounds shut down." She reached inside her purse and handed him a small package. "It's not much," she said, a deep flush darkening her cheeks. "I wanted to give you much more for your fifteenth birthday!"

Dakota slowly unraveled the shiny gold wrapping and stared at an arrowhead. "Been in our family all these years," Savannah told him in a rush. "It belonged to Sitting Bull. He chipped it himself."

Dakota looked up at his mother in surprise. He knew it was the only thing she owned that had belonged to Sitting Bull, the great chief of her ancestors, the Hunkpapas.

"Thanks," he mumbled, running his fingers over the stone. It was smooth and sleek, reminding him of

the shiny chrome on his father's new truck. He shoved it deep into the front pocket of his jeans and tried to smile, but it was like trying to break ice with his bare hand.

A pained look crossed his mother's face for only a moment, but it was long enough to draw a deep sigh from Dakota. He frowned, realizing how much he looked like her—the same dark features and slight frame, eyes watchful as a raven, mouth thinly drawn. He was nothing like his Irish father, a giant of a man with bleach-blond hair and eyes bluer than the sky.

Savannah brushed her hair back and gazed at a trail of blackbirds cruising overhead. Her eyes seemed as faraway as the disappearing line the birds formed in the sky. Something pulled and twisted in Dakota's gut, a feeling close to dread at having his mother back from Missoula and not knowing for sure if she was any better. He tried to toss the feeling away with a shrug. "See you back at camp," he said. "I'll be tired and hungry when I return, so have my supper ready." He managed a half smile this time.

"Get out of here," she said, swishing her hand at him. She turned and walked down the road, fading into the shadows of the tall bluffs, her figure growing smaller and smaller. Out of the darkness, Dakota heard her voice trail back to him. "Don't be calling out the ghosts. You just let sitting bulls lie, you hear me?" Her laugh echoed across the stillness.

Dakota turned down Battlefield Road, an uncertain grin stealing across his face. His mom had actually

laughed without effort. "Maybe she is getting better this time," he told himself.

He ran along Battlefield Road feeling charged, knowing he could run for miles and miles if necessary. Drops of perspiration trickled down the sides of his face and neck, soaking the inside of his T-shirt. A good feeling rose inside of him, fueling him with energy, pumping his legs faster and faster. It was good to get away from the calves that needed branding, the colts that were waiting to be broke, and the repairs that were adding up faster than the golden apples ripening on the trees. His grandfather, Jon-Jay, would have to manage without him today.

At the top of the slope Dakota sat down and crossed his arms over his raised knees. His breathing came short and fast, sounding like the labored snorts of his collie dog after a long run. He looked all around him and tried to familiarize himself with the terrain. Below him the Little Bighorn River flowed steadily along its winding path. On the other side of the river was the wide level bank where Major Reno and his men had charged the Indian village over one hundred and twenty years ago.

Dakota jumped to his feet, eager to cross the river so he could charge the two miles down the slope where Sitting Bull had massed the largest Indian village of all time. As he drew closer to the river, a cool pocket of air crept up on him, sending shivers down his back. Looking skyward, he saw black clouds massing together, totally blocking the sun. A gust of wind

whistled past him, sending branches and leaves whipping around him. He peered over his shoulder, expecting to see someone. But there was not a soul except him and an empty battlefield.

He stepped to the edge of the river and ran his hand through the water. Whoa! It was ice cold and running at a faster pace than earlier. He didn't care. He would cross.

Dakota untied his sweatshirt from his waist and held it high above his head before stepping into the water. The cold cut through, making him jump forward and cry out at the same time. Eager to reach the other side, Dakota plunged ahead, his chest and knees plowing through the current like a buffalo treading deep snow.

He scrambled up a steep embankment that jutted from the river's edge. At the crest a wide stretch of land opened before him. Shivering, Dakota searched for any sign of the sun returning. It seemed to have disappeared altogether, leaving dark purple clouds in its place.

Dakota pulled his drenched T-shirt over his head and wrung out as much water as he could. He slipped his arms into his bulky sweatshirt and sighed as the soft terry cloth lining dropped over his head and fell against his frozen chest.

He pulled the package Jon-Jay had given him earlier that morning from his hip pocket and tore the brown paper apart as if it were a candy wrapper. He frowned at the Swiss Army knife, his name engraved in fancy letters that swirled into one another: *"Dakota*

Miles," a name chosen by compromise between parents of different cultures. He turned it over and opened all the gadgets, the small scissors, the bottle opener, thinking all the time of the horse his father had promised him on his fifteenth birthday. He dropped the knife into his front pocket where he kept the arrowhead and wondered if either present would be of any use to him.

The broad hill sloped far below him. He wasn't sure he still wanted to charge down it. His tennis shoes and jeans made sloshing sounds whenever he took a step. He decided instead to follow the river upstream. It would eventually take him to a place where he could recross the river and join Medicine Tail Coulee to Battlefield Road.

Dakota followed the river as it twisted and turned in a northeasterly direction. On his right, high bluffs protruded from the river bank, blocking any view of the trail beyond. He continued another mile until he came to a narrow path between two steep knolls and followed it to the edge of the river.

A bolt of lightning darted across the sky, barely touching the surface of the bluff in front of him. The noise that followed was so sudden it caused him to fly backward and land squarely on his bottom, his back hitting something hard and solid. Dakota moaned and turned around slowly. He was up against a large black rock, about six feet high and four feet wide, its surface smooth and shiny. It reminded him of a fortress, but it seemed out of place among the smaller rocks and clusters of cottonwood trees.

Dakota leaned against the rock. A faint chirping

drew his attention to a dense thicket nearby. Leaves stirred restlessly as the sound rose to a sharp, persistent trill. Dakota rose and crept toward the sound. Squatting on his haunches, he parted the underbrush and peered inside. Staring back at him was a red-winged blackbird, its dark pelletlike eyes fixed on Dakota, unwavering in their keen observation.

Dakota reached inside and pulled the bird from the thicket. When he separated the feathers he discovered that its wing was torn, as if a sharp claw had sliced a line down the middle of it.

Another thunderous boom exploded all around him, making the ground vibrate. Dakota backed away until he was up against the rock. "Man-o-man-o-man!" he cried, drawing the bird close to his chest. Silver arrows streaked across the charcoal sky, followed by rolls of thunder that boomed like cannons during cross fire.

Dakota's feet slipped from underneath him as he slid down the embankment, the bird flying from his hands as he hit the water. The current tugged at him, sucking him forward, then swirling him around like a whirlpool. He thrashed at the waves as if they were wild beasts. The blackbird floated past him, its eyes dark specks against the raging white water.

A powerful force began to pull Dakota down. In a split second his hand seized the bird, and together they descended into the murky depths.

CHAPTER 2

Tatanka Iyotanka

Dakota struggled to pull himself from a deep sleep that held him to the ground. He raised his head and blinked several times against the blazing sun. Below him the river flowed as peacefully as the clouds drifting overhead. He squirmed uncomfortably in his damp, muddy clothes. Where in the world was he? Nothing looked familiar. He dug into the soaked pockets of his blue jeans and fingered the arrowhead and the outline of his pocket knife.

A faint chirping sent Dakota scrambling to his feet. A few yards in front of him was the blackbird, its crumpled body as soiled as a dishrag. He scooped up the bird and laughed nervously. "How did you survive that ride?" he asked, running his fingers over the damp feathers. Then he was struck by an even greater puzzlement: How in the world had he survived?

Dakota bit down on his lip and frowned. He realized that the river was different from the one he had left behind. There was less timber along the bank and clusters of sage opened to fields of lush prairie grass. "That's strange. How come everything looks so

different?" he wondered. One thing was certain: He was no longer at the Custer Battlefield. He wrapped his arms around his chest as a sudden chill rushed through him. Something was wrong.

Dakota gazed at the sun, trying to estimate the time. If he was right, it was midmorning. But how could that be? He had started his run down Battlefield Road late in the afternoon. Surely he hadn't slept a full day on the riverbank, or had he?

He slipped out of his muddy T-shirt and sweatshirt and ran them through the water. His reflection swayed back and forth with each gentle ripple. He grimaced when he saw his shoulder-length hair, tousled and matted, his face streaked with mud, a long gash forming an "S" down his cheek.

Struggling up the steep bank again, Dakota spread his clothes out to dry, all but his soggy jeans, which he kept on. When he stood, the ground rose and fell in waves. Overcome with nausea, he lay on the uneven ground and drew the blackbird close to his side. The sun and the stillness of the plains calmed him, settling him comfortably into the earth, a flush of summer air covering him like a blanket.

Dakota wasn't sure how long he slept, but something jolted him awake. He strained his ears, sensing danger. A rapid rumbling sound echoed in the distance, making the ground vibrate. He jumped up and stumbled, snatching his T-shirt and sweatshirt off the ground. He slipped them on and placed the bird securely in a fold of his sweatshirt. Before he could retrieve his shoes and socks, he froze as clamoring

hooves stampeded toward him. A cry escaped from his gut as two mounted Indians stopped about fifty yards in front of him, their bows drawn and arrows pointing straight at him. Dakota stared at the yellow and red stripes that stood out in hideous contrast against the black paint that covered their faces.

When the warriors started yelping, Dakota stepped forward, raising his arms in the air. Was this some kind of joke? He laughed nervously. "Hey! Are you part of the reenactment?"

The warriors didn't say anything. Instead, they began whooping louder and kicked their horses forward. Dakota wheeled around and started running with all his might toward the open prairie, his heart pounding hard against his chest.

The battering of hooves closed in on him as the war cries grew louder, drowning out all other sounds. As Dakota turned around to check the distance between him and his pursuers, a powerful force ripped through his clothes and skin, throwing him off balance. Stunned, Dakota staggered forward, then fell on his side. The blackbird made a plaintive chirp as it slipped from his sweatshirt and hit the ground.

One of the arrows had pierced the front of his left shoulder, the arrowhead penetrating only halfway into his flesh. Still he cried out like a trapped animal. Fear and pain choked the air from his lungs, squeezing him like a vise until it was impossible to breathe.

The Indians dismounted and shuffled toward him, their moccasins barely a whisper across the grass. Dakota bolted to his feet, wincing at the pain that

bore deep into the muscle of his shoulder. About twenty feet in front of him was a clump of bushes. He scrambled forward, holding the arrow as he ran.

A rope slipped easily over his head and fell to his hips, tightening around the top of his jeans and holding him to the ground. One of the warriors grabbed a handful of his hair and yanked his head upward. His face was within inches of the painted face, the eyes flashing with arrogance. Dakota drew back in surprise. They were only boys—probably no more than a year or two older than himself!

One of the boys grabbed the end of the arrow that protruded from Dakota's shoulder and broke it off. Dakota cried out in agony. He touched the wound around the edge of the arrowhead and felt his blood, warm and sticky. The Indians grabbed him by his arms and lifted him like a sack of grain, then threw him across one of the horses. His stomach slammed against the horse's back and his arms and legs dangled against either flank.

The young warriors mounted the other horse, and together they took off at a gallop, following the river upstream. Dakota bounced against the horse's back, each heavy thud knocking the air out of him. Between the tormenting pain in his shoulder and the pounding in his head, he prayed for a merciful end. He tried not to think of what lay ahead. His mind raced with the warning General Custer had given his men: "Fight to the death rather than face torture at the hands of your Indian captors." A feeling as black and raw as an Arctic winter froze his insides, making it more difficult to

breathe. What if Custer had been right? What other reason did they have to take him with them?

Dakota's body had grown numb and weightless by the time the Indians finally rode into their village. Hundreds of lodges at least fourteen feet high, with a dozen lodge poles crisscrossing out of the small openings at their tops, stood in a circular formation. When the women and children saw Dakota they stopped what they were doing and came running from all directions.

The warriors wrestled Dakota from his horse and dragged him by his arms through the dirt, then dropped him next to an open fire. Everyone was speaking at once in words that made no sense to him.

Dakota could barely stay conscious as the pain cut deeper into his shoulder blade, so deep he felt as if his arm were being torn off. In a state of half-awareness, he heard the voice of an older man speaking calmly, but firmly, while the young warriors continued to argue, their anger drowning out his softer words.

Suddenly, strong arms lifted Dakota from the ground. The man moved with sure, quick steps, his hold surprisingly gentle. He carried Dakota into a large tepee and placed him on a thick buffalo rug beside a fire, the flames sending long shadows dancing against the buffalo-hide walls.

The Indian stood over him, chanting words Dakota didn't understand. A drum beat nearby, matching the furious pounding of his heart. Dakota shivered. His shoulder blazed as hot as the white coals beneath the fire, while the rest of his body felt

like ice was cutting through it. He tried to concentrate on the figure before him, tried to determine if he could trust him. Someone called, "Tatanka Iyotanka." The words were familiar.

The man pushed a piece of rawhide into Dakota's mouth. It felt hard and bulky. He heard his sweatshirt ripping at the spot where part of the arrowhead was protruding. He grabbed the sides of the buffalo robe, terrified at what might come next.

In an effort to push the pain and fear away, Dakota concentrated on the words "Tatanka Iyotanka, Tatanka Iyotanka." Blinking several times, he tried to make out the features of the man before him. His frame was muscular and his shoulders broad. He had a flat, wide nose and lips drawn in a thin line. A strange feeling stirred inside Dakota. There was something about the man's piercing eyes that puzzled him. Silently he repeated the words again, "Tatanka Iyotanka, Tatanka Iyotanka." Raising himself to an upright position, Dakota stared long and hard at the man until he felt his heart jump. The kindness hidden behind those dark eyes was none other than Sitting Bull's!

Dakota lay down again, not making a sound, barely breathing. It was not so much out of fear that he did not move but from the realization that the world as he knew it had shattered into a million pieces. Sitting Bull was at his side, administering medicine to him. His eyes told him what his mind could not comprehend. And he wasn't sleeping.

Dakota tried to shift his thoughts back to the Little Bighorn River, to the storm that had hit with

such fury. It was as if some omnipotent power had warned him not to go farther, but he had plunged ahead anyway, until the angry river had swallowed him up, only to spit him out far from the Little Bighorn Battlefield.

A stabbing pain jolted Dakota upright. He bit down on the rawhide, forcing back his tears. Sitting Bull pushed against Dakota's chest, forcing him to lie down again. The blade cut through his upper arm quickly and evenly, like a steak knife cutting through tender meat. The sharpness of the blade burned so fiercely he wanted to scream. Instead, he bit down hard on the rawhide, almost tearing it in two, thankful that the arrowhead had not bored all the way through his shoulder.

Perspiration dripped steadily from his temples and down his back. He could feel his skin ripping apart as Sitting Bull extracted the arrowhead. The pain grew red hot and savage, his mind fuzzy. He let himself drift away from consciousness, away from pain.

Dakota awoke. A large shadow wavered in front of him. He sat up and tried to focus on the image. An involuntary gasp escaped his lips. It was really Sitting Bull! He had not been dreaming after all.

The chief was wearing only a breechcloth, and his broad chest was bare, except for a pouch hanging around his neck, made of badger fur and with four smaller pockets hanging from the bottom.

Sitting Bull lifted the back of Dakota's head and brought a buffalo horn to his lips. Dakota noticed that the chief's arms were red and swollen, with ugly welts running up and down either arm. He drank what was offered him, welcoming the taste and warmth of the liquid against his parched throat. It was similar to tea, only stronger, with an earthy flavor of fruit and wild flowers. Dakota handed the empty horn back to Sitting Bull, thanking him with a quick nod. He wondered if he should say something, but uncertainty held him back.

Sitting Bull pulled a small object out of one of the pockets on his pouch and held it up. Dakota drew back in surprise when he saw the arrowhead—the one that his mother had given him only yesterday. When he reached for it Sitting Bull drew his hand away.

"Hey! That's mine!" said Dakota. "Give it back." He cringed at the sound of his own voice, so childish.

Sitting Bull regarded Dakota curiously, then shook his head. Clutching the arrowhead firmly in his hand, he said, *"He mitawa."*

It was obvious to Dakota that Sitting Bull was claiming it as his own. He fell back on the buffalo rug in exasperation. His mother had given it to him, but it did belong to Sitting Bull. He smiled to himself, thinking of what Savannah had said earlier at the battlefield. "You just let sitting bulls lie." Well, that was exactly what he was going to do.

Without warning the chief tossed the arrowhead into the air and caught it in the palm of his hand. He flipped the edge of it with his thumb and forefinger

and sent it flying onto Dakota's lap. Dakota was about to say something, but Sitting Bull had already turned to leave.

Dakota stirred uneasily and stared around the tepee. Across from him were two empty buffalo rugs. He thought about his mother. She would be worried by now. She was probably walking up and down the battlefield calling his name, getting more worried by the hour. How was he going to get back to her? He didn't even know where he was.

For the first time Dakota noticed a bandage wrapped neatly around his left shoulder. Some blood had already drained through the heavy cloth, leaving a dull, red circle. He moved his shoulder in circular movements, surprised at how much better it felt.

Throwing the buffalo rug from his chest, Dakota stood up and stepped outside. The camp bustled with children and women working at various tasks near the smoldering campfires. Dogs wandered freely all over the village, their barking adding to the lively atmosphere.

Dakota wrapped his arms around his bare chest and looked down at his feet. He remembered that he had left his shoes somewhere alongside the river. He suddenly felt scared. Should he run away and try to find his mother? He looked up and down the village. Which direction should he take? As he hesitated, he saw a woman coming toward him, her face dark and wrinkled, and her frame so thin he imagined the slightest wind would topple her.

Dakota crouched low and tried to back his way

into the tepee, but the woman was fast upon him, her hand clamping down on his arm like a steel shackle. He looked down at the bony hand, cracked and dry like an old boot, and he felt his stomach turn. He tried to pull away, but the woman yanked him forward, saying, "*Uwa yo.*"

Dakota planted his feet solidly on the ground and leaned back. "What do you want?" he shouted.

The woman yanked him forward again with a roughness that surprised him. "*Uwa yo.*" she repeated, her voice harsher this time.

Dakota let the woman lead him to the riverbank. She pushed a large container against his chest. "*Mni,*" she said, pointing to the river.

Dakota guessed that she wanted him to fill the pouch with water. He made his way slowly down the incline and dipped the container in the river, filling it almost to the top. Since there was no strap on the pouch, he had to use both hands to carry it. The pain in his shoulder began to burn like a hot iron. He set the pouch down and pointed at his bandage.

The old woman made an ugly face at him. "*Uwa yo.*" she snorted, motioning him to follow. Dakota scowled back at the woman, but he did as she commanded. When they reached the campsite he was panting and his face felt hot and clammy. He moaned as he set the pouch at her feet, then slumped to the ground, his hand pressed against his wound.

The woman kicked him hard against his hip. Dakota jumped to his feet and waved a fist at her. The woman froze with her mouth open and her eyes wide.

He let his hand drop to his side and stared at his feet for a long time, knowing he had made a grave mistake. For a boy to threaten a Sioux woman in any way was strictly forbidden—a lesson his mother had reminded him of often enough.

The woman shot Dakota a warning with her dark eyes as she handed him another container. The thought of hauling water from the river again made his head spin. He couldn't do it. He shook his head, but the woman pushed and shoved him until he was heading once again to the river.

When they reached the embankment, Dakota shuffled toward the river, his chin resting on his chest, willing himself to make it one more time. The woman's voice rose shrill as a hawk, *"Hiya! Hiya!"* Dakota spun around, his arms pressing the pouch tight against his chest. The woman was shaking her head and pointing at the thick shrubbery above the riverbank.

Dakota returned to where the woman was standing and placed the pouch at her feet. She picked a few chokecherries from the trees and dropped them into the pouch, then pushed the container toward Dakota. He sighed, grateful that his task did not require the use of his left shoulder. As he plucked the ripe berries from the trees he surveyed the Indian village. The valley was dotted with tepees running as far as he could see to either side. Beyond the center of the village was an incredible pony herd, close to two thousand grazing on the lush grasslands.

Across from the southern end of the village, at

the edge of the valley, a cluster of sand-colored rocks towered over fifty feet high, standing in stark contrast to the low-sloping valley. The sight triggered some memory in Dakota, but he couldn't place it.

He wondered if he was still in Montana. The smoky blue sage that dotted the prairie and the wandering creek beds and cottonwood trees told him he was, but there were no road signs anywhere, no telephone wires, not even a building—nothing but unspoiled land.

"This is crazy," he told himself. There had to be a simple explanation for all of this. But what? Was he hallucinating? Was he suffering from a concussion? He felt around his head but discovered no sign of a bump or even a bruise.

Dakota continued to pick the berries until his hands were stained purple and the sun dropped behind the tree-covered bluffs. He groaned softly to himself, his stomach tight and burning from all the berries he had slipped into his mouth.

When the woman called to Dakota again he carried the half-filled pouch and followed her back to the tepee. She lifted the flap and Dakota slipped inside. He was too tired and sore to do anything but collapse onto the buffalo rug he had used earlier and fall fast asleep.

When Dakota awoke, a dying fire hissed and a thin gray light filtered through the opened flaps around the bottom of the tepee. He sat up and winced

as raw pain seared through his shoulder. He noticed that a new bandage had been applied while he slept. There was no longer any sign of seeping blood. He wondered if Sitting Bull had been in to see him while he slept.

The same two buffalo rugs were spread out, but only one was occupied by the old woman. Dakota stood, not making a sound. Was he free to come and go as he pleased? Or was he being held captive? Whatever the case, he was determined to get away. He had to find his way home. But how? The answer had to be somewhere along the Little Bighorn River, near Medicine Tail Coulee where he had fallen into the river. He remembered being caught in a swirling pocket of water that had sent him hurtling down the river at a speed he couldn't measure, while lightning and thunder had struck with such force.

Dakota froze as the old woman turned over in her sleep. He waited a few seconds, then tiptoed slowly past her and made his way to the door flap, his heart racing. Surely she would awaken at the slightest sound. For a second he thought of hitting her over the head, but he saw nothing that would serve as a weapon.

When he stepped outside the ground was cool and damp under his feet. The dusk hovered over him in a filmy cloud, so quiet it reminded him of the times he went hunting with Jon-Jay in the early mornings, the woods so hushed it was like being submerged in water. He had that feeling now that something was out there—ready to seize him at any moment. Squaring his shoulders, Dakota looked across the valley at a

hazy sheet of light rising over the bluffs. He would have to hurry before the others began to stir.

As soon as Dakota left the last tepee behind him, he kneeled in the tall grass and listened. Behind him a shuffling sound skimmed across the grass, followed by sharp barking. He threw himself to the ground and held his breath as a dog caught up to him and snarled as if threatening to rip open his throat. After a few moments, Dakota turned over and said softly, "Take it easy. I'm not going to hurt you."

The dog held its stance, leaning over him with its ears pulled back and growling deeply from its throat. "You've got to trust me," Dakota whispered, holding his hand out for the dog to sniff. "Wait for the ears to come forward," he told himself, remembering the warning his grandfather had once given him when a stray dog had chased him up a tree.

It seemed a lifetime before the dog finally sat down. Gradually, it drew its ears forward and its teeth disappeared as the muzzle closed and relaxed. He continued to speak to the dog until its tail thumped playfully against the ground. Dakota rose and continued making his way toward the towering rocks. For a while, the dog followed close at his heels, then stopped and watched as he slipped farther and farther from the village.

When Dakota reached the rocks, the silvery light of dawn was breaking through the darkness, exposing the outline of the village below. Already a few campfires were coming to life, sending the tangy smell of smoked wood and damp pine needles his way.

About thirty feet from Dakota, six towering rocks stood in a clustered mass, so powerful and mysterious it took his breath away. As he drew closer, it occurred to him where he had seen them! Two summers ago his mother had taken him to this very spot, telling him all about Sitting Bull's famous sun dance, which had taken place only three weeks before the Battle of the Little Bighorn. He remembered joking to Savannah that the rock on the far left looked like the profile of a conehead, presenting one mysterious eye and part of a smile.

Dakota had no doubt that these were the prehistoric rocks that Sitting Bull had once dreamed of, the place where he had led his followers. It was here that the Hunkpapa chief had predicted the outcome of the famous battle against General Custer and the Seventh Cavalry.

A cold sweat broke out on Dakota's forehead and trickled down the sides of his face and neck. He had been here before, but it wasn't the same. The dirt road he had followed to the rocks was gone, as was the house belonging to the landowner.

Dakota ran his hand over the smooth surface of the rocks, searching for the pictographs his mother had shown him. He found the Indians' drawings right away—the horses and soldiers falling into camp from the sky—as Sitting Bull had envisioned.

"Man-o-man-o-man! This is too weird!" he shouted at the prehistoric rocks. He circled around them slowly, searching for the pictographs of the Seventh Cavalry, which had also stopped here on its way to the

Little Bighorn Valley shortly after the Sioux and Cheyenne had left. His mother had pointed them out to Dakota, but no matter how carefully he looked, he could not find them.

Dakota scanned the valley below and watched the river as it flowed in a straight line beyond the village. The Rosebud? Wasn't that where the Sioux had camped during that famous sun dance? If he were correct, then General Custer had not yet made his way through this valley.

He remembered the bloody welts he had seen on the inside of Sitting Bull's arms when the chief was administering medicine to him. His mother had told him how the Hunkpapa chief had sacrificed one hundred pieces of his flesh to *Wakan Tanka*, Great Spirit, at the time of the sun dance.

Dakota hugged his chest as he drew a deep breath. What in the world was happening to him? And how was he ever going to get back home? He must be at least thirty miles from the Little Bighorn Valley. As Dakota wrestled with his confusion and fear, a sudden noise made him jump. He spun around and raised his good arm in defense as a dark shadow came crashing down on him, knocking him to the ground.

CHAPTER 3

Talking to the Wind

Summoning every ounce of strength, Dakota flung the intruder off his chest and sent him tumbling backward. From somewhere behind the rocks another person appeared and grabbed him by his arm and yanked him to his feet. Bellowing like a bull, Dakota charged at the boy, who merely stepped aside with foot raised and sent Dakota sliding across the ground, spitting up dirt and indignation. He looked up at the faces of the same two boys who had captured him earlier and stammered in rage, "Not you again!"

As he scrambled to his feet Dakota met their laughter with a single thought burning like a branding iron inside him: He would even the score if it was the last thing he ever did.

The old woman Toskala was leaning against her tepee when they reached the Hunkpapa village. As soon as she saw Dakota she flew at him like an angry rooster, shaking her fist and cackling so fast and furiously he knew he was in for another miserable day.

As Dakota had expected, additional chores were

added to further humble him. He was forced to fetch water, pick berries, and dig along the riverbank for turnips. Toskala provided Dakota with a turtle shell mixing bowl in which to make soap and a stone slab and berry masher for pounding chokecherries. When the shadows of evening darkened the plains, the old woman showed Dakota how to use a toothed flesher made of bone to cut away the fat and muscle from a buffalo hide. Next he was given an antler adz to scrape the inside until it was as smooth and soft as the belly of a puppy. All through the day he worked with his face set in stone and his mind set on escape, as he bore the sneers and ridicule of the village children.

On the seventh day of Dakota's captivity he woke to find a girl standing over the fire, stirring something in a deep pot. His stomach churned with hunger, and his mouth was so dry his tongue felt twice its normal size. He wondered if he should try sign language. Would the girl understand and give him something to eat? He was about to give it a try when she came toward him, carrying a bowl in each hand. When she offered one of the bowls to Dakota he snatched it eagerly and drank in deep gulps, spilling water down his chin. He could drink a river dry and still crave more.

Without a word or smile, the girl handed the other bowl and a horn spoon to Dakota. He was pleased to see that it contained stew similar to what the

old woman had given him, only this was thick with buffalo meat.

While Dakota was finishing the first meal he had enjoyed in days, Toskala strode into the tepee and gestured for Dakota to follow her. For a moment he thought about refusing her. He stepped back until his foot touched the edge of his buffalo rug, then plopped down as if the day belonged to him.

Toskala took a step, her head thrust forward and her eyes the dark, angry slits of a hawk. Dakota backed up against the inside covering of the tepee and turned his attention to the girl who was gathering various cookware items. When she looked at Dakota, her face was tight with anxiety, but an inkling of humor also played across her eyes. She gestured to him with a quick shake of her head, then instantly returned to her work. Touched by her concern, Dakota felt a rush of heat on his face. He scrambled to his feet and followed Toskala, stealing one more glimpse of the girl before stepping outside.

The brisk air and sportive mood of the village greeted Dakota at once, bending his mood toward merriment, then crushing it a second later. He focused his attention on a group of boys, no more than seven or eight years old, casting their small arrows over a hundred yards, while another handful of boys raced their ponies across the plains to a cluster of trees in the distance, then back again. Dakota longed to be a part of their sport, to show them how well he could ride, how well he knew the spirit and temperament of a horse.

As one of the boys broke out in front and raced toward the finish line, Dakota stood on his tiptoes and leaned forward. A steel hand grabbed his arm, turned him around with a jerk, and thrust against his chest a deer hide still damp with blood and tissue from a recent kill.

Dakota snatched the skin from Toskala and shuffled toward the fire. He found the usual implements waiting for him: the turtle bowl, the flesher, and the antler adz. Slowly and deliberately he lowered himself to the ground, wincing at the pain that shot through his shoulder. He began scraping away the fat and tissue with long, rigid strokes. His mind and body squirmed continually under the strain of discovering a way out of this tangled mess, but everywhere he looked he saw Indians, and more Indians. If he attempted escape, it would have to be sometime during the morning when most of the men were out hunting. He laughed out loud at the thought, aware of the hysterical ring in his voice. Even Toskala heard the strangeness of his laugh and hurried over to check on him and the progress of his work. Satisfied, she left with her pouch and headed toward the river.

Dakota bared his teeth and snarled at an imaginary foe as he scraped the last strips of fat off the hide. It seemed as if everyone in the village was having a good time—all but him. Even the young girls were playing contentedly with their miniature tepees and dolls, as the older girls laughed and shouted while enjoying a game that looked similar to hockey, only

their sticks were made of willow, the ends curved, and their ball consisted of pieces of buckskin rolled together in a round tangle.

Dakota sighed and reached for the antler adz. A movement in front of him caught his attention. He glanced up and saw a girl leading a beautiful bay to the front of Sitting Bull's tepee. She wrapped the lead rope around a stake just outside the tepee flap, but the horse pulled back nervously until the rope was a tight line from the post to its neck. Fascinated, Dakota watched as she ran her hands up and down its neck, then across its chest, speaking all the time to the animal as she caressed it with gentle words. Dakota smiled, happy to see that she understood the way to tame a horse was by gentle persuasion, not by a whip or harsh words. In only minutes she had the horse standing calmly, nudging her playfully on the shoulder.

There was something familiar about the girl, a gracefulness that made her seem untroubled, as if the world belonged solely to her.

The girl swung around and confronted Dakota with eyes as watchful as his own. He sat up, realizing she was the same girl who had offered him the water and stew, the one who had warned him not to resist Toskala.

He nodded once and tried to smile, but the bitterness of his situation forced his mouth into a tight line.

The girl made no attempt to smile back, but her face softened when she saw the work he was forced to

do. Her manner displayed none of the arrogance or mockery he had witnessed in some of the other village children.

Hoping to win more sympathy, Dakota ran his hands through his shoulder-length hair as he raised his face to the sun, emitting a long and exaggerated sigh. This time a hint of a smile crossed her face before she lowered her gaze and wrapped an arm underneath the bay's neck, drawing the animal closer. As she did this, the end of the rope loosened from around the stake, but the girl either didn't notice it or didn't care. She flung her long braids behind her shoulders and stooped down as she entered the tepee.

Dakota searched all around him, his heart racing. Toskala had already reached the river and had filled her pouch. He could barely make out her stooped figure as she straggled up the slight incline toward their campsite.

Dakota didn't take any time to contemplate the risks or ponder whether or not the girl had provided him an opportunity to escape. His decision was as clear and swift as the cry of a hawk. He flung the hide off his lap and bolted toward Sitting Bull's tepee, staying low to the ground. Using his good arm he hoisted himself onto the back of the horse and brought the rope bridle over its head, at the same time digging his heels firmly into its flanks. The bay bolted forward and slipped easily into a full gallop.

Dakota squinted against the morning sun and winced as pain ripped through his shoulder. Relying almost solely on his right arm, he stirred the horse

past two tepees, dodged a group of children, then shot across the hollow dale. The fresh air of midmorning smacked him full in the face, impelling him with confidence, as did the sturdy bay that seemed to understand his need to push forward at record speed.

From somewhere behind Dakota, a shrill cry penetrated the stillness, sending a cold wave of terror down his spine. He leaned closer to his mount and tried to put more life in his body so that the horse would do the same. He knew he would lose precious seconds if he looked over his shoulder, but he did so anyway, nearly falling off his horse. Pursuing him at a frightening speed was a warrior, naked, except for his breechcloth, his body curled low to his mount and his hair flying behind him like the tail of a horse.

Dakota scanned the horizon. Ahead of him the valley unfolded as far as he could see, offering no protection against flying arrows. To his right the mountains rose to a height too invincible to consider, while the Rosebud continued in a straight line to his left.

Dakota swung to the left and pleaded with his horse to make tracks. He wouldn't let himself be captured this time. If he wasn't able to escape by horse, then he stood little chance of freeing himself from the clutches of the Sioux. It was now or never!

The pounding of hooves grew louder and louder, as did a voice screaming inside his head, "Faster! Faster!" Sweat dripped down his temples and stung his eyes as he imagined an arrow ripping into his back, his body hurtling to the ground like a millstone.

Dakota scanned the distance to the river. Another

mile, maybe more. "I can make it! I can make it!" The hooves thundered against his ears. Closing his eyes, he struggled to remember the lessons of Jon-Jay. "Become one with your horse, move with it, feel the rhythm." Yes, that was it! His whole body eased a little and caught the timing as his arms and legs adjusted to the rhythm. The bay charged forward and swept across the valley like the wind.

As he neared the river, Dakota veered sharply to the right and headed upriver, searching for an easy crossing. Again the pounding of hooves drew closer, thundering against the ground, tearing up pieces of earth. Dakota cursed himself for not crossing earlier. The Indian trailing him would know this territory better than he.

He peered over his shoulder and let out a strangled cry. At that moment the Indian hurled himself onto Dakota and the two of them toppled from the horse, hitting the ground at the same time. Dakota rolled over once with the Indian practically on top of him, then pulled himself free. He was on his feet in seconds, groping for his knife, which was stuck in his pocket. "Damn!" he cried, his mind racing with the miracle that an arrow had not yet ended his pathetic life.

At last he freed the knife from its confines and flicked the blade out, confronting his attacker face to face. The boring eyes sent Dakota reeling backward. "Sitting Bull!"

The chief stood with his legs wide apart and his feet firmly planted. At his side he clutched a

double-edged knife, the silvery metal flashing bars of light at Dakota's feet. He squirmed uneasily, dismayed at the shades of exasperation clearly visible between the narrow slits of Sitting Bull's eyes.

Dakota felt his own anger rising and boiling over in frustration at his predicament, at the complete absurdity of what was happening to him. Unable to hold himself back any longer, Dakota started circling around the chief, spilling out the indignation that had been mounting inside him, weighing him down until all reason was lost.

"What are you going to do now?" he shouted at the chief. "My mother said you never hurt a woman or child! Is that true, or am I going to be the first?" He choked down his frustration by slamming the blade back into its groove, then deep into his pocket.

He continued to dance around the chief, taunting, "Come on Sitting Bull. I'm all yours. You might as well kill me now!" He let out an hysterical laugh. "I'm not going back with you!"

Sitting Bull grunted and motioned with a jerk of his head for Dakota to mount his horse.

Dakota crossed his arms over his chest and planted his feet wide apart, delivering the most defiant look he could muster.

The chief appeared dauntless as he sauntered over to Dakota and shoved him forcefully toward his horse.

Dakota swung around. "All right! I'll go back with you!" With the arrogance of his youth he narrowed his eyes at the chief and added in an undertone, "For now."

Once Dakota had hoisted himself onto the bay, Sitting Bull took the reins and led the horse to where his mount was munching contentedly on the grass.

"It's not over yet!" Dakota shouted over the chief's head. "I'll find another way!"

Sitting Bull mounted his horse and led them back to camp at an easy trot, not once giving Dakota the slightest notice. He might as well have been talking to the wind.

CHAPTER 4

The Pony Race

The following morning Sitting Bull slipped inside the tent with another man. Both were clad only in breechcloths and beaded moccasins. Dakota had no doubt as to the identity of the other man. His broad shoulders and chest were more pronounced than he had ever seen on anyone, and he stood well over six feet tall. He had to be Pizi, known to the white man as Gall, the great war chief who led the successful battles against Major Reno and General Custer at the Little Bighorn.

Sitting Bull circled behind Dakota and pulled from under a fold of the tepee his parfleche, a large painted bag Toskala had made to store Dakota's few personal items. The chief emptied it, dropping the Elton John T-shirt his mother had given him two years ago and his black sweatshirt, onto the floor. The warriors spoke to each other, their words flying back and forth as they turned the shirt over, then inside out, studying every detail of the lining and stitching.

Dakota held his breath, keenly aware of how strange his clothes must appear to the Sioux chiefs.

Pizi ran his hand over the sweatshirt, his eyes fixed upon the Sioux emblem that was stitched on its front. He turned and stared at Dakota with eyes that seemed to hold a mixture of suspicion and curiosity, even a hint of anger. Dakota felt certain this was a warrior he should avoid at all costs.

Sitting Bull tossed a small bundle onto Dakota's lap, saying, *"Hakicon."*

Dakota realized that he wanted him to put on the clothes. He searched the interior of the tepee for a place to change but found nowhere suitable. He looked to the chief, who merely waved his hand, gesturing to change at once.

Dakota left his buffalo rug, drawing his blanket around his waist at the same time. All he wore was his underwear. Surely they didn't expect him to change in front of them. He signaled with a twirl of his finger for the men to turn around.

Sitting Bull raised his eyebrows. *"Takuca?"* he asked in a firm voice.

Dakota let the blanket fall from his waist, with only his white jockeys to cover him. Sitting Bull and Pizi looked at each other and broke out in unrestrained laughter.

Dakota's lips tightened as humiliation burned across his face. He left his underwear on, picked up the strip of cloth, and let it roll out in front of him. It was about six feet long and a foot and a half wide. He searched for a buttonhole or loop to which he could fasten the belt, but he could find none. Now what? He

knew he held a breechcloth, but he had no idea how to get the stupid thing on. Maybe wrapping it around his waist and slipping the belt over it would work. He gave it a try, circling the cloth around his waist a couple of times, but when he stepped inside the belt and drew it to his waist, the whole thing unraveled and fell to his feet in a tangled heap.

Pizi said something to Sitting Bull, and both their faces twisted in laughter.

Dakota narrowed his eyes at Pizi and imagined what it would be like if he were strong enough to knock him over and watch him tumble to the ground. "That would wipe the smirk off his face," he thought with satisfaction.

Sitting Bull stepped forward and untied the end of the thong and belted it around Dakota's waist, looping an easy knot at the end. He showed Dakota how to place the middle of the breechcloth between his legs and pull the front and back up under the belt. He then pulled both ends down so that they hung freely in the front and back, falling inches above Dakota's knees, with the sides of his legs exposed all the way up to his waist. Dakota grinned as he stepped into the moccasins, pleased with their fit. It was as if they were made especially for him. Feeling more confident, he slipped his underwear off and circled around the inside of the tepee in his new attire, biting down on his lip to keep from smiling.

Sitting Bull and Pizi led Dakota outside. The plains glistened in layers before him, still fresh from

the morning rain. The air was cool and crisp, filling him with hope that this day might be different from those before it.

The warriors took him to where hundreds of ponies grazed. He inhaled the aroma of sweet ripened wheat and the sweat from horse flesh. As far as he could see, no human-made contraption of any kind spoiled the peaceful landscape.

Sitting Bull stopped about twenty yards in front of the herd, his eyes wandering over the choice selection. The heads of the ponies were large in comparison to their bodies, which stood only fourteen hands from the ground. Sitting Bull spoke a few words to a young boy, who dashed off toward the ponies, veering first to the right, then circling behind them. He slipped up to a solid black pony and grabbed a handful of its long mane, then led it back to Sitting Bull.

Sitting Bull called to another boy who answered to "Peeshkoh." The boy pushed past the other children in his hurry to reach the chief. Dakota drew back in surprise. He was one of the two boys who had roped and wrestled him to the ground like a runaway calf, then trailed him to the prehistoric rocks to recapture him.

While Sitting Bull talked to Peeshkoh, Dakota couldn't help but admire how tall and muscular the boy was. He thought bitterly of his own size, much too small and lean for his age, his muscles not yet developed the way he would have liked, despite all the hard work he did on the ranch. He guessed the

boy was part Indian, part Caucasian like himself, though Peeshkoh's eyes and hair were darker and his skin was the rich brown of a rough-winged swallow.

Peeshkoh turned to Dakota and pointed to the north. "We will race our ponies to that cluster of trees, circle around them, then return to this spot." He stomped the ground with his foot to indicate where they would finish.

Dakota stared at the boy in surprise. It was the first English he had heard in days. How happy those simple words made him feel! He drew closer to the boy, eager to ask him questions, but there was something in Peeshkoh's expression that told him to hold his tongue. There would be other moments to talk. Instead, he raised his injured arm and inquired, "How can I race like this?"

Peeshkoh scoffed, twisting his face in scorn. He turned to the others and spoke to them in what sounded like Lakota. The children started laughing, heckling him with looks of disapproval. Dakota searched the face of Sitting Bull, but he found no clue as to his emotions. The chief merely motioned with his head toward the black pony, signaling Dakota to mount.

One of the boys put a war bridle in the pony's mouth so that it fell below the lower jaw and looped to form a double rein. Dakota knew that this pony race would somehow mark his reputation in the village. No matter what, he must prove himself a better rider than Peeshkoh. It was his chance to get even.

Dakota took the reins from the young boy and began stroking the pony's neck, trying to determine the mood of the animal. Why had Sitting Bull chosen this particular pony? He held his hands underneath the animal's nostrils so that the two of them could get acquainted. He had little time to learn about his mount.

"I will need to walk with the pony—to get acquainted," he announced to Peeshkoh.

Peeshkoh turned impatiently to Sitting Bull and relayed Dakota's message to him. The chief nodded, his arms folded over his chest.

Dakota spoke gently to the black pony as he walked it away from the others. "You and I will ride well together, eh?" He ran his fingers through the thick mane, letting his weight rest against the pony's strong chest. "I am going to let you take the lead," he said, rubbing the pony's muzzle. "But, I will be a part of you, just the same."

Dakota pulled himself up on the left side of the pony, using his good arm as leverage. He gritted his teeth in pain, finally getting his leg over the pony and his body into an upright position.

A large crowd had already gathered, everyone shouting and talking at once. Dakota realized that they were making bets on the race. He was certain that no one would bet on him. He noticed that Peeshkoh sat tall on his black and white pinto, wearing the face of one sure of himself.

While the Sioux made their bets, Dakota had the pony trot in a wide circle around them, concentrating on the feel of his mount, on its attitude. The pony felt

happy and energetic. Dakota tried to make himself feel the same.

Peeshkoh spoke without pausing between his words. "We will begin at the sound of the arrow hitting its mark." He pointed to a small tree about one hundred yards in front of them. Dakota nodded, bending slightly over his pony's neck to stroke its muzzle. At that moment his eyes locked with Sitting Bull's. There was something warm and reassuring in their exchange, igniting a flicker of hope in Dakota.

Pizi had been chosen to shoot the arrow. He took quick aim, releasing his fingers from the bow string. The arrow made a whooshing sound, flying straight through the air before it hit its mark with a loud thud. In a split second the ponies charged forward, kicking up clouds of dust.

Dakota leaned forward, clenching his teeth as the pain shot through his shoulder. He shifted both reins to his right hand and let his left arm rest on his lap. He rode neck and neck with Peeshkoh the first quarter of a mile, then the other pony moved out ahead. For the time being Dakota would let Peeshkoh take the lead. All he would worry about now was keeping his pony at a smooth and even gallop on the first stretch.

The wind splashed against Dakota's face, charging him with energy. Driven by sheer willpower he pressed his legs against the upper flanks of his steed and wrapped his arms around its neck, whispering words of praise. The pony seemed to understand him as it lunged forward, quickening its pace until they were sailing across the prairie.

They were only a mile from the cluster of cottonwood trees. He saw that Peeshkoh was riding low to his mount, only five horse lengths ahead of him. Dakota knew that he would have to gain the advantage at the turn, keeping as close as possible to the edge of the trees, swinging sharply without losing ground.

When Peeshkoh began his turn, he kept close to the trees. Dakota had been counting on that and gave his reins full slack, letting his pony move toward the lead. He and his pony gained speed quickly and closed the gap in a matter of seconds. Dakota moved his steed close to the right side of the pinto, at the same time leaning to the left with his mount as they made the turn.

He stayed close to Peeshkoh, forcing his opponent closer to the edge of the trees. The nearness of Dakota closing in on Peeshkoh seemed to unnerve him as his pinto fell behind and dust swirled in his face.

Dakota leaned still closer and nestled his face against his pony's drenched neck, letting his bare knees hug its taut shoulders. They were moving together, each sure of the other's power. He no longer felt any pain—only exhilaration. He had a strong urge to whoop like a warrior in battle.

The pounding of hooves drew closer, thundering against his ears. Out of the corner of his eye Dakota glimpsed the head of the pinto, only a few yards behind him. He forced himself to relax, to give no indication to his pony that he was tightening up. It was a sure way to force his mount to do the same. Another lesson from Jon-Jay.

"Not much farther," he told himself. "Come on, Black Pony," he cried. "We can do it!"

Dakota saw the crowd ahead of him, a cluster of swaying bodies, arms raised like flags, waving wildly. The need to win burned so deep inside of him it hurt.

Hammering hooves pounded behind him, drawing closer and closer. Both ponies were neck to neck, their mouths foaming. Dakota cursed under his breath. It was all or nothing now.

Dakota let his buttocks and thighs move with the pony, up and down, up and down. He leaned as far forward as he could without falling off, feeling the pace quicken. He let the reins slacken all the way, and the pony took the final stretch on its own.

Dakota closed his eyes, the thundering of hooves heavy in his ears. Loud whoops and hollers rang out on either side of him. Slowing his pony gradually, Dakota opened his eyes and circled wide before trotting back to the excited group. He had no idea if he had won or lost. His hands still clutched the pony's mane, his knuckles as white and cold as the fear inside of him.

Peeshkoh rode up alongside him, breathless and flushed. "It was close," he said. "The others say you won by a nose."

Dakota made his face look hard in order to hide the joy that swelled inside of him. Peeshkoh slipped off his pony and walked toward the corral. There was no animosity on his face this time, only resignation.

Dakota felt as if his lungs would burst. He tried to stop his legs from shaking, but it was no use. Now

that the race was over, the pain reawakened in his shoulder, doubling him over.

He noticed that everyone was slapping Sitting Bull on the back, handing him tobacco pouches and pipes. Even Pizi handed over an armful of goods. It occurred to Dakota that Sitting Bull may have been the only one who had bet on him. The possibility filled him with pride.

Then Dakota thought of something else. Sitting Bull had known all along that he stood a good chance of winning. He smiled to himself, remembering how he had given the chief quite a run along the Rosebud. Looking skyward he whispered, "Thanks, Jon-Jay."

Dakota watched as Peeshkoh strode toward him. He had already turned his pinto loose with the rest of the herd. His war bridle hung from around his neck, bouncing against his broad chest. Dakota stood his ground, feeling pangs of self-consciousness as the boy drew closer to him.

"What is your name?" asked Peeshkoh.

"Dakota."

"You ride well . . . better than you run." Peeshkoh grinned, his manner easy this time. "Sitting Bull says that the black pony is yours." He turned to go, then stopped. "Tomorrow there will be a buffalo hunt. We leave at the first sign of the sun."

"Buffalo hunt?" echoed Dakota, but Peeshkoh was already leaving.

Dakota walked to the pony corral in a daze. He had never ridden so fast, or been so sure of himself. It was as if he were riding on the wings of time, racing

horses as his grandfather had done when he was Dakota's age.

Something fluttered inside of him when he thought of the buffalo hunt. He gave his pony a solid slap on the rear, releasing it back to the herd. "If only Mom could see me now. . . ."

CHAPTER 5

Guiding Spirit

Dakota had been awake for hours, keeping a sharp lookout for the first sign of dawn to slip into the tepee. But time crawled slowly, bit by bit, drop by drop, until the agony of lying still drove him out of bed and scrambling into his breechcloth and moccasins. He grabbed his sweatshirt and slipped outside.

A gusty wind whipped across the prairie, driving its cool energy through him. On the horizon a layer of soft, silvery light surfaced along the rocky peaks. Today would be another test of his bravery. Dakota was sure it was the reason he had been asked to accompany the warriors on the buffalo hunt. For the time being he would play along with them. There was no way he was going to let an opportunity like this slip past him. Sooner or later he would get out of here and return to Roundup.

He forced his thoughts back to the upcoming hunt. Did Sitting Bull expect him to kill a buffalo? He wrapped his arms around his chest and let the idea swell inside of him. He had killed an elk once with a Ruger 30-06 rifle. The Sioux would use the bow and

arrow, and probably the lance, in their quest. They probably had a few guns, too.

He remembered that when he had moved to Montana his grandfather had taken him hunting, mostly for rabbits. Jon-Jay had given him his first and only lessons in archery. Dakota smiled when he thought of how his arrow kept slipping off his bow, how Jon-Jay kept at him all day until he was able to shoot the blasted thing at least thirty yards.

Dakota scanned the horizon. The sun was climbing from behind the mountains, softly lighting up the plains. A gentle rustling caught Dakota's attention. He squinted against the fuzzy light of dawn, drawing into focus the figure of Sitting Bull. Around his waist hung a three-inch belt made of thick hide and containing a number of leather cases. Dakota could see that the chief carried a knife and an awl case, but he wasn't sure what the other cases contained. In his left hand was a lance at least two feet taller than the chief. The grip was wrapped in buckskin with two eagle feathers adorning the lance's top.

Sitting Bull signaled Dakota to follow him, so he hurried after the chief, who took long, quick strides. They arrived at the same place where the pony race had occurred the day before. Dakota hesitated when he saw that Peeshkoh was there. He was carrying two short bows and two quivers, each containing ten arrows. The quivers were tubular in shape, with a soft buckskin bow covering attached to each one.

Sitting Bull spoke to Peeshkoh, then pointed to the cluster of sand-colored rocks in the distance.

Peeshkoh stepped closer to Dakota. "Tatanka Iyotanka wants to see how far you can cast an arrow," he said.

Dakota looked from Sitting Bull to the young warrior. What if he said no? Would he be excluded from the hunt?

Peeshkoh kicked the dirt and scowled.

"I know a little," said Dakota, letting his eyes wander to the distant rocks. He thought of the young boys he had seen the other day, shooting arrows so fast and far he had difficulty following their flight.

Sitting Bull handed him a bow and three arrows. The bow was only three feet long and felt light in his hand, the back painted a deep blue and the front a bright yellow. "Make your arrows go swift and far," Peeshkoh instructed Dakota. "We will see how much strength lies in you."

Dakota grinned. "Whatever you say," he replied, thinking that Peeshkoh was taking this matter way too seriously. He ran his hand over the arrow. It was silky smooth, like the wood railing on his front porch at home. Three wild turkey feathers adorned the end of the shaft. Dakota spun the arrow around with his fingers, admiring the fine craftsmanship. "It would be something to learn how to make these," he thought.

Taking a deep breath, Dakota concentrated hard on the task before him. He slipped the groove of the arrow into the bowstring and took the arrow tip between his index and middle finger, then extended his left arm as far out in front of him as it would go. He pulled back on the bowstring until it touched the

side of his right cheek, then aimed the bow slightly upward to get more distance. When he released the bowstring it pinged loudly, whipping harshly against his cheek. A sharp pain ripped through his shoulder as well, causing him to wince.

Dakota followed the arrow as it flew across the sky, then dropped no more than fifty yards in front of him. Rubbing his burning cheek, he shrugged apologetically to Sitting Bull, who merely stared at the fallen arrow with a face that held no clue as to what he was thinking.

"Here," said Dakota, reaching for another arrow. "Let me try again. I can do better."

Sitting Bull ignored him and took out his own bow and one of his arrows. Dakota watched closely as Sitting Bull gripped the bow handle with his left hand and brought the tip of his index finger just underneath the base of his thumb to form a circle about the size of an acorn. He slipped the arrow through the hole and drew it back, securing the groove of the arrow in the center of the bowstring. Placing the bowstring between his right thumb and forefinger, he drew it all the way back to the edge of his cheekbone.

"You must make your hands and arms work together," Peeshkoh instructed Dakota. "Push with your left arm and pull with your right at the same time."

Sitting Bull released his arrow, sending it whizzing through the air at an incredible speed. In a flash, he drew four more arrows from his quiver, sending each one flying in quick succession. Dakota shook

his head in awe as the last arrow reached its peak before the first one touched the ground.

Dakota wanted to give it another try, but neither Peeshkoh nor Sitting Bull asked that of him. Instead they exchanged hurried words with one another. "You must learn how to use the bow and arrow before you can go on a buffalo hunt," said Peeshkoh. "Tatanka Iyotanka says that you must learn to shoot straight and fast."

He stared open-mouthed at Sitting Bull, not wanting to believe that the chief would dismiss him so easily. Wasn't he the first to rise before all the others? Even before the sun had risen over the mountains?

Dakota grabbed Peeshkoh's arm as the young warrior turned to go. "What if I watch from my pony? I've never been on a buffalo hunt before."

Peeshkoh yanked his arm free and exchanged words with Sitting Bull. Twice Dakota caught the chief studying him with such keenness it made him squirm. Then he shook his head with great emphasis, his eyes unwavering. "*Hiya*," he said.

"There will be another group going out in a few days," said Peeshkoh. "You must practice the moment the sun rises and continue until it disappears behind the mountains."

Was that a smirk Dakota saw on Peeshkoh's face? He wasn't sure.

And then they were gone, leaving him alone with his bow and quiver and an ache in his stomach. He couldn't believe it. He watched Sitting Bull and Peeshkoh as they headed for the pony corral. Already

the young warriors were rounding up their mounts, eager to begin the hunt.

Dakota snatched his bow and quiver from the ground and stomped off in the opposite direction, toward the river. He wanted to break the bow over his knee, to hear it crack and split apart, the same way his hope had been shattered.

Instead, he ran—pumping his arms and legs, putting as much distance between him and the village as possible. The longer he ran, the better he felt. When he neared the river, he flung his bow and quiver onto the ground and flopped down beside them. Already a number of village children were playing joyfully in the water, while women gathered roots and berries along the bank.

Dakota studied the river as it rushed by, wondering about its final destination. Taking a few deep breaths to calm himself, he carefully went over in his mind the techniques Sitting Bull had used in handling the bow and arrow. He had only a few days to learn before the next buffalo hunt, and he would—no matter what.

All day long Dakota shot his arrows through the air, each time sending them farther and farther. He was becoming more comfortable with the timing— pushing with his left arm and pulling with his right, each movement in perfect harmony with the other. When he felt better about shooting the arrow straight

and far, he worked on his speed. He knew that a fine archer could shoot at least four arrows into the sky before the first even hit the ground. He did not expect to accomplish such a feat, but if he could master at least two at the same time he would be satisfied.

The night came quickly upon Dakota. He had practiced all day with his bow and arrows, not taking time to eat. Only an occasional drink from the river and a cool swim offered him relief from the endless day.

When Dakota returned to the village he was powerfully hungry and sore, and his arms hung limply at his side. At the campsite he hesitated, feeling awkward, as if he were intruding upon a private gathering. There were hundreds of men, women, and children feasting on the fresh buffalo killed that day. Laughter and high-pitched voices rang across the two-mile stretch of the village—happy, carefree sounds that only sharpened his isolation.

Dakota couldn't help but notice how generous the Plains Indians were with one another. Regardless of who succeeded or failed during the hunt, the meat was shared equally among all the people, the most tender pieces going to the elderly.

Dakota made his way past the throngs of people until he reached what was now considered his tepee, the one next to that of Sitting Bull and his family. He still wasn't sure if the old woman was a relative of Sitting Bull, or someone he merely looked after. He suspected it was the latter.

When he slipped inside the tepee he sighed with relief when he found it empty. He retrieved the eating

utensils that were now a part of his personal belongings and headed back to the campfire.

Helping himself to buffalo stew and cooked corn, Dakota took heed not to fill his plate to overflowing. Searching the immediate circle of Hunkpapas, he noticed that no one was paying him the least bit of attention. He returned to the tepee and sat on his warm buffalo bed, not caring that he was alone. Most of his childhood had been spent with few friends and no brothers or sisters with whom to share the long days. He had grown comfortable with solitude, at times preferring it to companionship.

Dakota devoured the stew like a hungry wolf, gulping and swallowing fast, not taking the time to savor the wild tastes of the hunt. Satisfied, he wiped the back of his hand across his mouth and sighed. He listened as the ground began to vibrate with the steady beat of drums and the soft pounding of feet swishing and spinning around and around, making his head reel. This is their busiest time of the year, he thought, with the start of the sun dance, followed by many celebrations and endless hunting expeditions. Dakota smiled to himself. If he had to be held captive by the Sioux, there was probably no better time than this to hang out with them.

Dakota's thoughts drifted to the upcoming buffalo hunt—to the black pony that felt so good beneath him. Above the pounding of the hooves, the plaintive cry of a bird grew louder and louder, drowning out all other sounds and sights. A sheet of black swept past him, followed by a splash of red.

Dakota bolted upright, his body damp and clammy. He shivered as an image of the blackbird, wet and crumpled, flashed through his mind. He knew, without knowing why, that he had to find the blackbird if he wanted to find his way back home.

Dakota slipped into his breechcloth, torn sweatshirt, and moccasins, careful not to awaken the old woman who snored softly into her buffalo rug. He pulled his pocket knife from his parfleche and tucked it into the belt of his breechcloth.

The village was hidden in a gray mist that sprinkled his face with tiny droplets. The air tasted faintly of pine, making his nose tingle. Dakota wasn't sure where to look for Peeshkoh, or how he was going to convince the boy to take him to the place where he and his friend had cornered him like an animal—but he had to try.

At the edge of the Hunkpapa village Dakota stopped abruptly. The young girl he had encountered a few days earlier was standing under a willow tree, using a strip of hide to groom the same horse he had stolen from her. He wasn't sure if he should turn around or not. In equal measure, confusion and shame weighed heavily within him. He was no longer sure if she had left the horse for him. Maybe she had even alerted Sitting Bull that he was fleeing the village.

After a moment of deliberation, Dakota took a tentative step forward, then trudged toward her, his

nerves as feverish as the certainty inside him that he was about to make a complete fool of himself.

When he drew within a few yards of her he stopped and cleared his throat. She turned and regarded him with indifference, then returned to the care of her horse.

Somewhat encouraged by the fact that she had not lunged at him or sent him a disgusted look, Dakota joined her on the other side of the horse and began stroking its mane. "She's a good horse," he said, pressing his face against the mare's muzzle. He knew the girl had no idea what he was saying, but perhaps she would appreciate his love of horses and his need to make things right between them.

An awkward silence followed as they both continued to fuss over the horse. Dakota stepped back and tried to smile, but his shyness held him in check. Remembering the purpose of his mission, he asked her in a deliberate voice, "Peeshkoh? Do you know where he is?"

At first the girl gave him a look of uneasy puzzlement, then she nodded slowly. *"Han,"* she said, pointing north. She started walking in that direction with her horse, so Dakota followed, admiring the long braids that fell to her hips and the easy way she moved.

It wasn't long before they stopped in front of a tepee that faced the river. The girl turned to Dakota and said, *"Leta."* She signaled with a nod of her head, then swung easily onto the horse and headed back. Dakota watched her go, regretful that the sparse Lakota he knew was of little help to him.

Dakota waited at the riverbank, keeping a watchful eye on the tepee. When Pizi emerged, his bare chest and arms bulged with muscles, reminding him of a gladiator. Dakota wondered how Peeshkoh came to share a tepee with the great war chief.

Moments later Peeshkoh emerged, a bow in one hand and his quiver slung over his shoulder. Dakota jumped up and called out to him in a loud, shrill voice. Peeshkoh swung around and stared at him with eyes that simmered like the grim, yellow gaze of a wolf.

When Peeshkoh made no effort to move, Dakota shuffled toward him, his resolve slowly crumbling under the boy's steady glare. When he was within a stone's toss away, Dakota cleared his throat and ran his hands up and down his thighs. "I need to return to the place where you found me," he blurted out.

Peeshkoh's face darkened. "You are *witkotkoke!*" he sneered. "You belong to Toskala. It is for her to decide where you go."

Dakota let his face show his disgust. "She can't tell me what to do!" he cried.

Peeshkoh gave him a contemptuous look. "You fetch her water, pick her berries. You do what she says."

Dakota let his eyes wander downstream. "For now," he mumbled. He reached into his pocket and took out the Swiss army knife Jon-Jay had given him. He pulled each gadget out carefully, as if their value were a rare thing to behold.

"If you take me there, I will give you this," Dakota said, holding the knife out as an offering to Peeshkoh. "I need to go back and look for a wounded blackbird.

It was with me when I crossed the river. As soon as we find it, I will come back with you." Dakota's face burned with the peculiarity of his request. Why was he making such a big deal about a bird, anyway?

Peeshkoh reached for the knife and examined it more closely. "Did you get this from the *wasicus?*" he asked, suspiciously.

Dakota knew the word for white man. It was one of the words his mother occasionally used with a touch of bitterness in her voice. Dakota shrugged. "Yeah, that's where I got it."

Peeshkoh continued to examine the knife. He seemed hesitant to accept the offer. "You are willing to trade this?"

Dakota thought of Jon-Jay driving all the way to Billings to purchase the knife, then having his name engraved on it. He imagined the care he would have taken in choosing just the right one. Dakota shook his head in disbelief. "Yeah, I'll give you my knife if you'll take me to the place where I lost the blackbird."

"*Hoppo,*" Peeshkoh said, waving his hand for Dakota to follow him.

In no time at all, the rope bridles were on the ponies and Peeshkoh and Dakota were loping across the open plains, not a word passing between them. The morning air turned hot and stuffy, bringing with it the pesky flies that buzzed all around them. Dakota groped for a plan of action. Though he longed to participate in the next buffalo hunt, the need to find his way home burned inside of him. Should he try to make a break for it once he found the bird? He

already knew how well Peeshkoh could ride, how well he could fight. He was sure Peeshkoh would use his bow and arrows if the need arose.

As soon as they approached the riverbank, Dakota recognized the narrow bluff where he had laid his clothes to dry. He searched the area, but there was no sign of his shoes and socks, or the blackbird.

Peeshkoh dismounted and Dakota did the same.

"Don't do anything stupid," Peeshkoh warned, casting a somber look at Dakota that made his breath catch.

Not far from where the bird had fallen, Dakota spotted a cluster of bushes. Dropping to his hands and knees he parted the brush and peered inside.

"The bird is gone," said Peeshkoh, kicking at the dirt. Still, he knelt and searched with Dakota.

Peeshkoh broke the silence by asking, "The blackbird? Is it your guiding spirit?"

Dakota sat up. "Guiding spirit?"

"Yes. Does it watch over you?" Peeshkoh demanded, a sharp edge to his voice. "A guiding spirit watches over me," he explained in a softer tone. "If I see and hear with my heart, then my guiding spirit will help me find my way."

If Peeshkoh hadn't looked so serious, Dakota might have laughed. He had never given much thought to a spirit looking out for him, let alone a bird. It was the same foolish talk he often heard from his mother.

From deep inside a chokecherry bush, a soft chirping broke out unexpectedly. Dakota and Peeshkoh

looked at each other in surprise. Dakota dug deeper into the underbrush until he saw the familiar eyes blinking at him, and the thin sharp beak opening and closing with each feeble chirp. Dakota pulled the limp body out and held it close. The feathers were like matted leaves sticking to his chest. "He's barely alive," he said, struggling to keep his voice steady.

Peeshkoh grabbed the mane of his pony and swung himself easily onto its back. "Take the bird to Tatanka Iyotanka. He is a good medicine man—even with animals."

Dakota thought about how well his shoulder was healing and nodded his agreement. "There is no Indian as great as Sitting Bull," he declared.

Peeshkoh studied Dakota in the same manner Sitting Bull had after he failed the bow and arrow test. "Where are you from?" he demanded.

Dakota faltered, not sure what to say. Roundup, Montana, didn't even exist yet. "A place far away," he muttered.

"Where is your family?" Peeshkoh asked, pressing for more information.

Dakota looked down at the bird and began stroking it. "I don't really have one," he mumbled. He squared his shoulders. "I'm on my own now, that's all."

Peeshkoh nodded, apparently accepting Dakota's explanation. "I left home two winters ago to get away from my father," he offered. A shadow crossed his face. "He is *wasicu*, a bluecoat." Peeshkoh spit the words out like they were foul bits in his mouth. "My mother is Lakota," he continued in a softer voice. "She

had no chance once her family arranged the marriage with my father. He spent more time drinking whiskey and beating her than he did hunting or working." Peeshkoh squinted his eyes. "One day she left without a word to either one of us."

"Did she go back to her people?" Dakota asked.

Peeshkoh shrugged. "She would have tried to find our winter camps, but no one has seen her."

"When did you leave?"

Peeshkoh pulled roughly on his quiver, adjusting it on his shoulder. "I should have left when my mother did. When I was sure she was not coming back, I took my father's best horses and rifles and gave them to Pizi. He took me in and made me a member of his family."

Peeshkoh was quiet for a moment, his head cocked as if he were listening for something. "*Hoppo,*" he said, suddenly. "We must get back to camp before Toskala comes looking for us."

The thought of the old woman left a bad taste in Dakota's mouth. He was tired of being ordered around by her. If he wanted to escape, he would have to do it soon. At the first opportunity he would break away and try to find his way home.

A silence settled between the boys as unbending as the path they followed. On one side, the river rushed forward in a straight line, its course firmly set. To their left, the jagged bluffs carved a barrier between them and the open plains beyond.

Dakota knew that Peeshkoh would eventually turn to the left and pass over the bluffs to get to flat land.

"As soon as Peeshkoh begins his climb, I will hold back a little," he thought. "When he is near the summit I will swing around and ride like I've never ridden before."

Dakota wrapped the blackbird within the fold of his sweatshirt, praying the bird would be safe as he made his escape. He tried to think of something casual to say to Peeshkoh, but he was afraid his voice would give him away. The song "Good-bye, Yellow Brick Road" played over and over in his head. He wiped a line of sweat from his forehead, trying to remember the exact words of his mother's favorite song.

When he reached the incline Peeshkoh stopped and readjusted his quiver over his shoulder. "Stay close to my mount and keep your thoughts away from trouble," he said in a gruff voice.

"Whatever you say," Dakota croaked. He waited until they had gone a few paces, then held the pony back, a little at a time. Keeping his eyes fixed on the hind legs of the pinto, he waited anxiously, ready to break away as soon as the pony began scrambling over the crest.

Dakota felt as if his legs were detached from his body. He slapped his thighs, trying to shake the fear away. "Any second now," he told himself. "Stay cool. Don't do anything stupid."

At the top of the crest, the legs of the pinto buckled as it lunged forward. Dakota swung his pony around and dug his heels into its flanks. He had to lean all the way back as the pony zigzagged down the steep bluff, stumbling over loose rocks and almost spilling Dakota onto the ground.

A cry erupted somewhere behind Dakota, throwing him off balance. He flew forward, grabbing the mare's thick mane, and pulled himself up. Behind him, the ground seemed to be crumbling, sending loose dirt and stones tumbling down the bluff.

Dakota glanced over his shoulder and watched in astonishment as Peeshkoh came rolling down the bluff like a runaway tumbleweed, his arms and legs flying every which way. Dakota strained his eyes against the glaring sun and saw two Indian boys, mounted and armed with bows and arrows, staring down at him. When their eyes met his, they gave a blood-curdling cry and started down the bluff.

Dakota spurred his mare, sending it flying down the bluff. When he reached the bottom, Peeshkoh was already getting to his feet and bolting toward him. Dakota kicked his mount hard and leaned forward, sending dust swirling behind him. He'd been waiting for this chance.

"Dakota!" cried Peeshkoh, his feet pounding the ground like a tight drum. "They will kill me!" Dakota squeezed his eyes shut, but the cry of Peeshkoh seared through his chest.

He reined his pony in, skidding to a halt in a swirl of dust and confusion. As soon as Peeshkoh was mounted behind him, they took off at a full gallop, dodging boulders and clusters of cottonwood trees that lined the riverbank. Peeshkoh's breath was hot against his neck. "Crows!" he cried. "If we make it to the edge of our camp, they will not risk coming any closer."

Dakota's heels dug into his pony's flanks as he

kept his eyes peeled for level ground. The sound of distant hooves grew louder and louder, as did a voice inside of him demanding to know why he had stopped for Peeshkoh.

"Head for the steep bluff over there," instructed Peeshkoh, crossing his arm in front of Dakota to show him the way. "Once we are climbing, it will be difficult for them to shoot at us."

"Whatever you say!" Dakota snarled. He wondered for the hundredth time how this could be happening to him.

"Now!" cried Peeshkoh. The hair on Dakota's neck prickled against his skin. He swung the pony to the right and pressed his knees tightly against his mount, his heart pounding as loudly as the hooves that pursued them.

"Man-o-man-o-man! They're going to kill us!" Dakota whimpered, feeling their pace slacken as the shrill cries of the Crows beat like hellfire down his neck.

Suddenly, halfway up the bluff, the cries ceased, as did the scrambling of hooves behind them. From the top of the ridge, Chief Pizi sat on his black stallion, his bow drawn and arrows flying so fast they whooshed past Dakota like bird wings. He looked over his shoulder and watched the young Crows racing back the way they had come.

When Dakota and Peeshkoh reached the top of the bluff, Pizi met them with eyes bristling with reproach. His words were surprisingly calm when he spoke to Peeshkoh, yet it was clear that something

unsettling was passing between them. Dakota was sure that if it were his own father confronting them, there would be more than mere words being exchanged.

When they returned to camp, Pizi left them without saying a word. Dakota squirmed with the realization that he had somehow led Peeshkoh into a confrontation with Pizi. At the pony corral, he risked asking what had happened to make Pizi so angry.

Remorse clouded Peeshkoh's eyes. "It was my duty to keep watch at the south end of our village," he said, "not lead the Crows into our camp." Peeshkoh waved the pocket knife in front of him. "I let *this* take me from my duties." He tossed the knife at Dakota, like one ridding himself of something distasteful. Then he added with a voice sharp with accusation, "You could have escaped."

Dakota looked away. "You wouldn't have needed my help if it weren't for the blackbird."

Peeshkoh reached out for the bird. "Give it to me," he grumbled. "I will take it to Tatanka Iyotanka and we will see if it was worth all this trouble."

With a feeling of regret, Dakota handed the blackbird over to Peeshkoh, then turned to leave. It was time to confront the old woman now, to accept the punishment he almost believed he deserved.

CHAPTER 6

The Buffalo Jump

The arrow whizzed off Dakota's bow and skimmed across the sky in a perfect arch, reaching its peak before the first arrow hit the ground. Sitting Bull nodded, a hint of satisfaction crinkling the edges of his mouth. *"Waste,"* he said, then exchanged a few words with Peeshkoh.

Dakota rocked back and forth, biting down on his lip.

"You can go," said Peeshkoh, grinning in a way that made Dakota wonder what meaning lay behind it.

Dakota followed Sitting Bull and Peeshkoh to the pony corral. He took the bridle from around his shoulders and moved easily among the horses, careful to hide the smile that tried to stretch across his face. "It is a good day to be alive," he thought.

Dakota was glad that Sitting Bull and Peeshkoh were among the hunting party, along with Pizi, three other men, and three additional boys. He recognized one of them as having participated in his capture. Peeshkoh called him Tahteh. He was smaller and looked younger, with a face that always seemed on the verge of laughter.

The band set off at a light trot, following the river in a southwesterly direction as it twisted like a snake. Hunting scouts took the lead, leaving the younger boys to trail behind. Dakota rode alongside Peeshkoh and Tahteh, hoping that Peeshkoh would talk to him, or at least introduce him to his friend.

Finally Peeshkoh broke the silence. "Today we are going to drive the buffalo over the cliffs. They will not be able to run from us then. Yesterday we drove them to a nearby pasture. We will find the buffalo there today, still feeding on the thick grass."

Dakota thought about what Peeshkoh said. It sounded too easy. He had been expecting a great chase, with the buffalo scattering everywhere—each hunter pursuing the animal of his choice.

"Will we get to chase them?" Dakota asked eagerly.

"The men will chase them," replied Peeshkoh. "We will remain at the bottom of the cliff, ready to send our arrows deep into their hides."

Suddenly the horses came to a halt. The men stopped and dismounted. They got on their hands and knees and searched the ground. Dakota wondered what they were looking for.

"There has been a hunting party ahead of us," said Peeshkoh.

"How do you know?" asked Dakota.

"There are tracks to the right of the horses. Crow by the outline of their—." Peeshkoh scrunched up his face. "I do not remember the word," he said, pointing to his moccasins.

Sitting Bull raised his hand and whispered, *"Inila."*

The warriors got back on their horses without making a sound. Dakota's mouth felt dry. Something was about to happen.

Sitting Bull rode to the center of the group and spoke only one word.

Dakota did not know what the word meant, but he didn't like the sound of it. He searched for Peeshkoh, who was now on the other side of the cluster of horses, next to Pizi.

At that moment Pizi and a warrior named Lutah Tahcha slid off their horses without making a sound. Staying low to the ground, they moved like snakes toward a thick cluster of bushes. The others remained on their horses, not moving, not making a sound.

Peeshkoh rode over to Dakota and bent close to him. In a whisper, he said, "We are going to attack."

"Attack?" Dakota let the word settle in his brain. "We're going to attack," he told himself. He searched the faces of the other young warriors. They were all alert, unusually quiet. They are all ready, he thought. Ready to fight. Dakota swung his pony around, then came to an abrupt halt when a powerful hand grabbed his reins. Startled, he looked up and came face to face with Sitting Bull, his eyes so close they burned into his, warning him to be quiet.

When Pizi and Lutah Tahcha returned, they spoke a few words to Sitting Bull, who in turn raised his lance high above his head and cried, *"Hokahe!"*

All at once the horses fell into single file, with Pizi leading the way toward the cluster of trees. Dakota fell to the back of the line, numb with fear.

Peeshkoh was in the middle of the formation, too far ahead to ask him any questions. He would have to watch and see what the others did.

A war cry spread from the front of the line to the back. All at once everyone took off at a full gallop. The first five horses swept to the left, while the other five, which included Dakota's, veered to the right.

"Man-o-man-o-man! What do I do? What do I do?" The words boomed like cannonballs in his head. He watched Tahteh in front of him. His arrow was set on his bow, his knees guiding his pony.

Dakota felt for his quiver. It hung freely on his back, flopping up and down as he galloped. He swung it over to his left side and fumbled through the opening until his fingers touched the feathered tips of his arrows. He grabbed two and slipped one between his teeth and the other he tried to steady on his bow. His hands and knees shook so badly he couldn't set the arrow straight.

In a haze he heard a sudden cry, then everything fell into chaos. His pony came to an abrupt halt, throwing him forward and causing his arrow to fall from his bow and hit the ground. Tears of panic stung his eyes.

The Crows were obviously as surprised as Dakota. They scrambled for their weapons and rushed to get to their horses. Dakota could barely see through all the dust. Behind him a clearing opened and he saw Peeshkoh chasing two of the Crows' horses toward the river.

He wiped the dirt and dust from his eyes and

scanned the immediate area. Something moved. He swung around. A few yards in front of him were two horses tethered to a tree. If he could get to them, he might be able to count his first coup. He knew that counting coup was the most important step that a young warrior could take in demonstrating his bravery and skill. It usually required touching the enemy first with a coup stick without injuring or killing him. Another way was to capture the enemy's weapons or horses, "A far better choice," Dakota thought.

Already half the Crows were mounted and fighting back furiously, their lances and war clubs swinging and slashing through the air as their battle cries echoed across the valley. Dakota swung his pony to the right of the unguarded horses. Seeing no one, he reached for the lead ropes, but one was caught on something. He gave it a hard yank, but it wouldn't budge. He sat still on his pony, watching and listening as if mesmerized. He slipped his pocket knife out of his quiver and cut the rope in half.

Seeing no one nearby, Dakota led the two horses away from the camp. He had gone only a few yards when he stopped. Something moved behind the bushes. He pulled his reins back, forcing his pony to step backward. Before he could turn around, a dark shadow came charging toward him, knocking him from his mount. Dakota fought blindly, thrashing out, trying desperately to strike the person on top of him.

Their bodies rolled back and forth on the ground. One moment Dakota was on top, the next his

attacker was. As they rolled through the dirt, Dakota glimpsed the face of his assailant. He was only a boy, younger than himself.

The young Crow managed to get Dakota's left shoulder in a deadlock. At the same time he pressed his knee into the middle of Dakota's back and raised his arm above his head. Dakota screamed out in pain and anger, at the same time glimpsing a flash of silver. With a mighty thrust he rolled to his side, taking the boy with him. The knife flew out of the boy's hand, striking a rock with a soft ping. Dakota smashed his hand into the boy's face, squeezing it as hard as he could, his nails digging into skin.

Dakota pressed harder and harder until his muscles were taut. He grabbed a nearby rock, hesitated a second, then brought it down on the boy's head. The impact made a dull thud. Sickened by the sound, Dakota dropped the rock and stared at the still body. A bloody welt was already forming on the boy's head. Dakota placed his hand close to the boy's mouth and sighed with relief when he felt warm breath.

He fell against his pony, his legs shaking from the uncertainty of what he had done. He was certain the boy would live, but what if he had struck harder? Could he have killed him?

Dakota grabbed the lead lines of the two horses and mounted his own. At a full gallop he headed in the direction Peeshkoh had taken, his legs pressed tightly against his pony's flanks. The river lay about a mile ahead.

What had just happened both shocked and

thrilled Dakota. He didn't want to hurt the boy, but he had to defend himself. He closed his eyes as the wind whipped across his face and imagined himself a warrior, like Sitting Bull.

Water. He needed it badly. Peeshkoh and Tahteh were already at the river. They waved to Dakota as he drew closer and slowed his horse down.

Dakota slipped off his pony and handed the two horses to Peeshkoh. He was bursting inside. The river sparkled clear and silvery before him. He stripped off everything but his breechcloth and plunged into the water, descending until his hands ran across the rocky bottom. He stayed within the murky depths until his lungs felt like they would explode. When he couldn't hold himself under any longer, he blasted through the surface. Cupping his hands under the water, he scooped handfuls into his mouth and drank greedily.

Dakota pulled himself out of the water and strode toward the others. Drops of water glistened over his golden brown body, which felt stronger after only a week with the Sioux.

Peeshkoh also seemed pumped up, eager for more action. Dakota could tell by the way he was talking, how his voice grew louder and his words rushed together, making it impossible to keep up with him.

Peeshkoh handed the reins back to Dakota. "They belong to you now," he said, his eyes bright with admiration.

Tahteh ran his hand across one of the horse's backs and whistled. It was obvious that he liked the gray mare Dakota had snatched.

The sound of hooves pounding the ground announced that the rest of the party was returning. Their cries of victory were a sign that they had fought well against the Crows.

Lutah Tahcha held his lance across his lap. Dakota noticed that something long and dark hung from it. As the warrior drew closer, he noticed dark hair wet with blood. He covered his mouth and looked away. Lutah Tahcha displayed his trophy for all to see—the scalp of his enemy, the Crow. Pizi also carried two scalps at the end of his lance. Though Dakota understood the Lakota believed the hair was an extension of the soul and the taking of a scalp meant the soul of an enemy was forced to remain on earth rather than ascend to the spirit world of Wakan Tanka, he still couldn't help the cold ripple of fear that raced through his veins when he thought of losing his own scalp. Despite the disgust Dakota felt about such an act, he let the feeling go when he saw that everyone else was in good spirits, ready to resume the buffalo hunt.

Pizi led the way once again, taking them into a light trot. They followed the river until they reached a shallow grassland that sloped upward. In the distance, jagged mountains soared into the sky, their black steeples a stark contrast to the milky-blue sky. The late morning had moved into midday, with the sun beating down on them in hot waves.

"We are close," Peeshkoh whispered, pointing in front of him. "The buffalo are beyond those hills."

Sitting Bull signaled for everyone to stop, then gave instructions for the ensuing hunt. Dakota

watched the others, envious that they understood the words of Sitting Bull and he didn't. He decided that he would ask Peeshkoh to teach him Lakota. Perhaps in exchange he could give him one of his horses.

At the crest of the hill the party stopped. Dakota had to hold his excitement in check. Never before had he seen anything that matched the magnitude of the sight below. At least a thousand beasts grazed lazily across the prairie, their shaggy coats of dark chocolate like roving mountains. The bulls stood at least seven feet high where their shoulders arched, the cows as much as six feet. It seemed impossible that he was here, witnessing one of the greatest moments in their history. He bent down and pulled a tuft of grass from the ground and marveled at that as well.

Sitting Bull instructed Peeshkoh to lead the boys around the back of the pasture to the bottom of the cliff, which dropped at least twenty feet. They would wait there while the men drove some of the buffalo over the cliff.

Peeshkoh found a place far from the fall area to tie the horses and ponies. He explained that they needed to be far enough away so that the buffalo could not catch their scent.

When the young warriors arrived at the buffalo jump, Peeshkoh made sure that they were all a safe distance from where the buffalo would drop. The five of them were spaced about twenty feet apart, forming a large horseshoe around the enclosed pasture. With their bows and arrows set, they waited.

At the far corner of the horseshoe, Dakota faced

the jump, trying hard to steady his breathing, to get his heartbeat to slow down so he could think. What if the fall didn't kill or injure all of the buffalo? How much time would he have to cast his arrow? And what if he missed? No time to reload, no time to run. Instant death. His heartbeat quickened, pounding against his chest like a drum.

Something shook and rumbled above him, a sound similar to the beginning of an earthquake. Dakota looked up, expecting to see the cliff crumble into bits. But it was unusually quiet, the thundering coming from farther away. It seemed to be moving in on him, pressing closer and closer. Fear settled like a stone in the pit of his stomach.

One of the boys shouted, *"Pte!"*

Dakota knew the word for buffalo. They were coming! The thundering hooves rolled toward them with such force it seemed as if the cliff would break apart. Instinctively, he stepped backward: one, two, three steps, with his eyes steadfastly watching the circle of boys. They too were moving backward.

The rumbling exploded above them. Dakota steadied himself as the ground vibrated. Dust rose and billowed into heavy clouds that opened suddenly, displaying the shaggy heads of the buffalo. Their hooves skidded along the edge of the cliff as they tried desperately to stop their fall. It was too late. Their front legs flew in front of them as their heads rolled behind their shoulders, as if they were looking behind them. Deep bellowing cries followed, filling the hollow pocket of the cliff with a deafening pitch. As the back

legs of the buffalo slid off the cliff, their bodies fell forward and they plummeted head first. In midair they rolled over once before crashing down on their backs or sides, hitting the ground like fallen trees.

Twelve buffalo fell from the cliffs. Some of them lay still, either dead or too wounded to move. Others continued to bellow loudly, clawing furiously at the ground in an effort to get up.

As he stepped backward, Dakota rubbed his sweaty palms against his breechcloth. Slowly he drew his bowstring back to a ready position. In front of him a young buffalo cow was struggling to rise. As he drew nearer, his eyes locked with hers. All he could see were dark pools of pain and fear, similar to what was probably reflected in his own eyes.

Dakota scanned for the last rib behind the left shoulder. He tried to steady himself so that his hands and legs wouldn't shake, so that he could send his arrow deep into the animal and erase the frightened look from her eyes. He pulled back on the bowstring and released the arrow a little too early. It drove deep into the buffalo's neck, causing her to roar out in pain.

"Kill her!" a voice deep inside him screamed. The next arrow wouldn't hold still. He bit down on his lip and tasted blood. "Steady, steady," he told himself. He drew his bowstring back and took careful aim. When he found the center of his target he released his arrow. It flew straight and fast into its mark and made a loud sucking noise as it broke through the thick hide, leaving only the feathers exposed. The buffalo gave a violent shudder, then dropped her head, exhaling her last

breath of life. Dakota went over to the buffalo cow, bent down, and ran his hand over her head. It was thick and woolly, like the sheep back home.

Something moved, followed by a thunderous crash that sent Dakota scrambling to his feet. He swung around and in the nick of time saw the hulk coming. Rage steamed from the bull's nostrils as it pawed the ground, its red eyes flaring before it lunged forward. Without thinking, Dakota dove over the buffalo he had killed and hit the ground with his arms outstretched. He slid across the dirt, wincing at the pain that seared through his shoulder. At the same time the buffalo bull whipped around the dead cow and stopped less than ten feet away from him, his head lowered, ready to plow through anything that got in his way.

There wasn't any time to get off the ground. Dakota held his last arrow up, ready to stab the bull. All at once two thousand pounds of muscle came charging at him. In that split second Dakota thought, "I'm dead." With every ounce of energy left in him, he hurled his body out of the way. A crushing weight slammed against his lower legs, smashing his stomach and chest hard against the ground. Choking and gagging, Dakota tried to crawl out from under the dead weight. He clawed at the earth, but he couldn't move. Looking over his shoulder, he gasped in horror. The massive head of the buffalo lay staring at him across his legs, but the eyes were like black stones at the bottom of a river, cold and lifeless.

Then he saw the arrow sticking out from behind

the animal's left shoulder. Through the haze of dirt and dust, he saw Sitting Bull helping the other men pull the buffalo off his legs. Once the pressure was lifted, Tahteh and Peeshkoh helped lift Dakota to his feet. At first his legs collapsed underneath him, forcing the boys to hold him up. He took one step, then another. Gradually, he was able to stand on his own. He surveyed the carnage before him. Every buffalo that had fallen from the cliff lay sprawled across the ground in twelve gigantic heaps, none of them moving.

Since the women had remained at camp, the task of butchering and preparing the carcasses for transport had already begun by two young warriors who were helping Pizi turn a buffalo onto its stomach. Pizi cut the hide at the nose and ran the knife along the center of the back all the way to the tail. Next they cut and rolled strips of hide one over another into tight bundles, ready for transport.

Pizi cut into the belly of the buffalo and pulled out the liver, still hot and bloody, and handed it to Tahteh. The boy bit into the tender meat with gusto and grinned as blood dripped down his chin.

Across from Pizi, Sitting Bull was doing the same, pulling the liver out of the young cow Dakota had killed. He handed his knife to Dakota, the liver hanging from the tip, wet and steaming.

Dakota held back, shaking his head, trying to tell Sitting Bull that he didn't want it. But the chief only grinned and pressed his knife against Dakota's chest. The liver was wet and warm and stuck to his skin. He grabbed the knife and stared at the bloody organ,

thinking how much better it would taste if it were cooked over a fire.

"What are you waiting for?" demanded a harsh voice next to him. He turned to see Peeshkoh glaring at him, his upper lip curled in contempt. "Is she your buffalo?"

Dakota stared at the cow, her eyes dark and vacant, the rest of her a large skeletal husk. "Yeah, she's mine," he said, rubbing his thigh. He pulled the liver off the knife and took a small bite, closing his eyes. It was slimy and rubbery in his mouth, the blood leaving a sour taste that made him gag. When Dakota opened his eyes, he realized that everyone was watching him. He chewed slowly, afraid to swallow for fear of getting sick. He made a choking sound as he handed the knife back to Sitting Bull. From the corner of his mouth, he managed to mumble, "I'll finish it later."

As Dakota walked away, he cringed at the laughter that followed. He spit the chewed liver into his hand and tried to brush his shame away by telling himself that things could have been worse. He might have been killed by that buffalo, gored to death only a week or so after his fifteenth birthday.

The hunters made a lot of noise as they rode back to their village. They were all stripped down to their breechcloths, their copper-brown backs and shoulders glistening, their muscles broad and taut. They rode with great energy, yet at the same time with great ease.

Several of them sang out in booming voices that echoed across the valley.

Dakota rode at the back of the line where he could watch the others. The prairie grass stood at least three feet tall, swaying back and forth as if it were dancing. Soft blankets of cotton grasses peeked out in clusters, their willowy tufts blowing all around them like a flurry of snowflakes, while the music of meadowlarks and warblers filled the air with the joyful sounds of summer.

"It is impossible not to love a land as beautiful as this," Dakota thought. Could it be the endless fields of green and yellow that had such a calming effect on his spirit, his soul? He wasn't really sure what part of him it touched. He only knew that it filled him with gladness and made him feel a part of the world.

Dakota inhaled the beauty around him, wondering why he was following so eagerly behind the Sioux, not giving a single thought to escaping. He shook his head, clearing his drowsy contentment. If his mother had been here and shared some of what he had felt, she'd be better in no time.

Dakota searched the front of the line until he found Sitting Bull. He was bent over his horse, laughing hard at something, his body shaking with pure joy. It was amazing how Sitting Bull often seemed to be where the fun was. "Well, why shouldn't he be having a good time?" thought Dakota. "Life on the plains in the early summer of 1876 couldn't be finer."

CHAPTER 7

The Moon of the Chokecherries

It seemed to Dakota that the village was growing as fast as the chokecherries were ripening, with a handful of people arriving each day, adding their boisterous clamor to the procession that swelled from one mountain peak to the next. He learned from Peeshkoh that there were seven bands of Indians already gathered for the summer festivities and celebrations. They included the Cheyenne and six bands of Sioux: the Oglalas, the Brules, the Sansarcs, the Minneconjou, the Blackfeet, and finally the Hunkpapas. Many of them had left the reservations in search of Sitting Bull's trail, eager to recapture a way of life that was disappearing as quickly as the buffalo.

Dakota decided to ask Peeshkoh right away about teaching him Lakota. His desire to learn more about the Sioux was as great as his need to express himself in their tongue. He found Peeshkoh near an open fire at the Hunkpapa camp, where women and girls were preparing the buffalo hides and making pemmican. He

slipped alongside his new friend and moved right to the point. "Do you like either one of the horses I took from the Crows?"

Peeshkoh eyed Dakota suspiciously. "Why?"

Dakota tried to sound casual. "I thought we might make a trade," he offered.

Peeshkoh's eyes lit up. "What kind of trade?"

"If you teach me Lakota, I'll give you one of my horses."

Peeshkoh didn't say anything at first. Instead he turned and faced the pony corral. His gaze followed the herd until he found what he was looking for. His face was set in hard lines as he contemplated the offer. "Will you give me the white stallion?"

Dakota's eyebrows shot up in surprise at Peeshkoh's choice. He tried to read the expression on his friend's face, but he could find no clue as to why he wanted this horse. It was obvious to Dakota that Peeshkoh had not observed the finer qualities of the gray mare.

"You want the white stallion?" Dakota asked, making sure he had not misunderstood.

Peeshkoh crossed his arms over his chest. "That is the one I want," he said.

"We've got a deal?" asked Dakota, extending his hand to Peeshkoh.

The young warrior stared at his hand without taking it. He gave Dakota a playful shove, causing him to stumble backward. "I will teach you Lakota in exchange for the white stallion."

Peeshkoh moved closer to the fire where one of

Sitting Bull's wives, Four Robes, was cutting into a large hunk of buffalo. Dakota followed, not yet finished with the conversation. As if reading his mind, Peeshkoh turned to him and said, "We will begin tomorrow when the village moves. There will be plenty of time to learn on the road," he concluded.

"We're leaving?" asked Dakota, more disappointed than surprised. He was beginning to feel comfortable at this familiar spot.

"We leave in two days, at the first sign of the sun," stated Peeshkoh. "We will follow the buffalo south as they look for new grasslands."

Dakota considered what Peeshkoh said. Of course they would move. In all the excitement during the last few days he had forgotten what lay ahead. They were making their way toward the Greasy Grass, or the Little Bighorn Valley as the *wasicus* called it. He shook away a sudden chill and dismissed General Custer and his bluecoats from his mind.

Many children pushed and shoved as they tried to get close to Four Robes. They shouted and waved their horn-shaped cups in front of her, trying to get her attention. Dakota wondered what they wanted. Without warning, Peeshkoh shouted over his shoulder, "Wait for me. I will be back." He took off like a deer, tall and sleek, sweeping across the prairie in leaps and bounds.

Dakota squeezed among the children, eager to know what was happening. Four Robes held a knife in her hand, its handle made of crudely carved wood, the blade long and silvery, casting bars of light that

danced among the children's shadows. She set the tip of the blade into the center of the buffalo's stomach and made a clean cut, about the length of her index finger. As soon as the blade punctured the thick hide, a profusion of blood spurted out like a waterfall, filling the rawhide container she held under the incision in a matter of seconds. Pink foam gathered at the rim, spilling over the sides and splattering to the ground.

The children pushed forward, waving their cups back and forth. She filled each one to the rim. Dakota watched in disbelief as the children drank the steaming blood as if it were milk. They smacked their lips and sighed, drinking until their cups were completely empty.

Peeshkoh arrived just as the children were finishing. He stepped in front of Four Robes and held two cups out to her. Dakota slumped to the ground. "He can't possibly expect me to drink that!" he thought.

Peeshkoh handed a cup to Dakota. "This is 'wi-yatke,' 'cup,'" he said, grinning. Dakota took it from him and repeated the word, "Wiyatke." He peered inside and laughed nervously. As he expected, it was filled to the brim with thick buffalo blood. "Are you really going to drink this?" Dakota asked, staring at Peeshkoh as if he were crazy.

"Damn right!" said Peeshkoh, placing the cup to his lips and gulping loudly.

Dakota grinned. "You sound like my father, and you act like him, too."

After Peeshkoh had drained his cup, a red mustache remained above his upper lip. He wore a smug

look when he said, "Pizi takes me with him when he trades with the *wasicu*. I am learning to speak like one, right?"

Dakota laughed. "Damn right!"

Peeshkoh ran his tongue across the blood, then let out a loud belch. Some of the children laughed in appreciation. Dakota turned away. "He's jerking me around again," he thought. "It's just another test."

"We call this '*we*,' 'blood,'" Peeshkoh said, forcing the cup to Dakota's mouth. "Drink it. It's good for you."

Dakota made a disgusted face, scrunching up his nose. Through the corner of his eye he caught Sitting Bull, his bare chest puffed out like a brown bear, pushing his way through the crowd until he stopped three paces in front of Dakota. "*Yahepa!*" he said, lifting his hand to his mouth in imitation of one drinking.

There was something in the way Sitting Bull spoke and the keen way he regarded Dakota that commanded respect. Closing his eyes, he swallowed a mouthful of the blood. Nausea churned inside him as the warm blood gushed down his throat and thickened in the pit of his stomach. He had no way to describe the taste. All he could identify was a creamy, salty flavor that rose from the back of his throat, threatening to gag him. He forced his mind from the image of the blood and made himself believe it was juice from a hamburger. "I'm drinking hamburger juice," he told himself, shutting his eyes and taking another gulp.

Sitting Bull crossed his arms over his broad chest and waited for a response. Dakota wiped his mouth with the back of his hand. He remembered the word

for "good." "*Waste*," he choked out. His smile was thin and stiff.

Sitting Bull nodded, looking pleased.

"*Waste*," repeated Dakota, holding down a burp that rose in his throat. His stomach turned and rolled like a raging storm, ready to spill everything from his gut. There was no way he was going to finish it.

He backed away from the others, careful not to draw attention to himself, at the same time impatient to get away from the smell of blood. He found himself drawn back to the circle of girls who were busy preparing the buffalo hides. He found a place close to the fire where he settled comfortably on his side, his legs curled behind him, the storm in his stomach quieting down. When he was sure neither Peeshkoh nor Sitting Bull was watching him, he emptied his cup into the thick buffalo grass, then slid away from it.

He watched as the girls cut long strips from the buffalo meat, then hung them over elevated stakes to dry. He leaned on his good arm, feeling lightheaded under a perfect sun and welcome wind that brushed across his face.

One of the girls crept toward the buffalo with her hand raised in mock ferocity. With the speed of a bird taking flight, she swept her hand across the buffalo hide and struck it forcefully, imitating one counting coup. The other girls laughed and goaded her on. Dakota realized she was the same girl who owned the beautiful bay. For a split second their eyes met and she smiled.

Dakota looked around him to see if the smile was

meant for someone else, but there was no one near him. He felt a gentle stirring inside him, as soft as a butterfly's wing, teasing him. When he thought of what Peeshkoh had told him earlier that day, he winced. He had only hinted at the idea that he liked the young girl who was so attentive to the horses, that she seemed different from the other girls. Peeshkoh had frowned, advising him that she was Many Horses, the eldest daughter of Sitting Bull, and he should stay away from her. "Do not even look at her," he warned.

"Well," reasoned Dakota, turning his eyes back to the young girl, "looking isn't going to hurt anyone." Besides, he would be returning to Roundup soon. Maybe he would even visit Sarah Red Feathers this summer. It had been almost a year since they had played softball together with some other kids at the Standing Rock Reservation. He smiled when he thought of the picnic they had shared along the Grand River, how she had pushed him into the water and jumped in after him. They had held each other under, trying to see who could stay under the longest. In some ways Many Horses reminded him of her. They were both a little shy and a little bold at the same time, and they both had a way with horses.

From the distance, clouds rolled eastward, melting into one another and forming great billows that swallowed chunks of the clear blue sky. A breeze nipped across the prairie, cooling the air and stirring something deep inside of him.

Sitting Bull came and sat next to Dakota. He seemed as intent in watching the young girls at their

tasks as Dakota. Neither said a word or tried to communicate. They were content with the quiet that settled between them.

The entire buffalo now lay in hundreds of long strips that hung from a five-foot-high structure. Once it dried, the buffalo would be pounded and mixed with animal fat and wild chokecherries to make pemmican, the same hard sausage that Toskala had taught Dakota to make.

A long shadow flickered above, causing both Sitting Bull and Dakota to look skyward. A golden eagle soared directly above them, circling once, twice, then two more times. Its wings extended at least six feet as it cried, "Kya-kya." Dakota felt a fluttering in his stomach, as if the wings of the eagle were inside him. The sensation cut through him, leaving him speechless and bewildered. The bird cried out one more time, flying so low the shadows of its wings darkened the ground. It hovered close, then darted upward, beating its wings into the wind, becoming smaller and smaller, until it was only a gray dot on the horizon.

Dakota pressed his hands against his chest to stop the fluttering that beat inside him. He turned to Sitting Bull to see if he too had been affected. The chief reached across Dakota and placed his hand over his chest where his heart beat and said, "Da ko tah," patting his chest with each syllable. He waved his hand toward the sky as if gesturing to the heavens. "Mitakuye oyasin," he said, the sound of the words drifting inside of Dakota like a mystery.

Dakota nodded, his eyes damp. He was certain

that Sitting Bull somehow understood that he was from another place, from another time. "Yes," Dakota whispered, making a wide sweep with his hand. "I am from far away."

They sat facing one another, an understanding passing between them. It was not necessary to draw upon words. Dakota felt secure with what he saw in Sitting Bull's eyes. He was sure that the chief understood that he was searching for something, for an answer to a question that was as old as time itself: the meaning of his life.

The spell was broken when a handful of children came barreling at Sitting Bull, tumbling him over. Some of the children held the warrior's arms down while two young boys pretended they were shooting him with arrows. Sitting Bull cried out in mock pain, burying his head in his arms. At that moment the children climbed onto his back, hooting and hollering at the top of their lungs.

From the other side of the Hunkpapa village, Pizi lumbered over, swinging his arms like a grizzly bear. A young boy and girl, about five and seven, followed closely beside him. Dakota supposed they were two of his three children.

When Pizi yelled across the field, Sitting Bull jumped up, sending all five children tumbling off his back and onto the ground. He bent down so that he was level with them, his eyes dancing like fireflies in the night. "Nuwe unyinkte," he said.

The children jumped up and down, shrieking their happiness at the top of their lungs. Sitting Bull

lowered his haunches and bellowed in imitation of the animal he was named after. The children flew toward the river, flapping their arms wildly. Sitting Bull followed, glancing once over his shoulder as if to let Dakota know that he had not forgotten him.

An achy feeling tugged at Dakota, a yearning to be part of their happiness. Sometimes he wondered if there was something wrong with him. Why did he have such a hard time fitting in with others, even with his own family? His own father had not yet invited him to Alaska, choosing instead to bring his new family to Roundup for a brief visit.

An image of Jon-Jay flashed in his mind, the old man in his baggy overalls and straw hat, pounding fence posts into the ground, his muscles firm and bulging, and his mood as cheerful as the sun beating down on him. It was curious how neither the extreme weather conditions of Montana nor Dakota's abrupt mood swings could draw a negative response from his grandfather. And Dakota knew that he could be a real pain sometimes. In some ways Jon-Jay was a lot like Sitting Bull. They both spoke in a quiet manner and each possessed a world of patience.

Dakota watched as Sitting Bull and the others stripped off all their clothes. Pizi lifted his son high above his head and tossed him playfully into the river. The boy came to the surface spurting water from his mouth.

The tightness in his stomach forced Dakota to his feet. He made his way to his tepee, wondering if he would run into Many Horses. It didn't really matter

that he did not yet know her language. Even if he did he would be lost finding just the right words to say to her.

True to Peeshkoh's word, early the second morning the seven bands of Indians began early preparations for moving the village. Hunting buffalo was the driving force behind every move, followed by the need to find fresh grazing for the pony herd that numbered in the thousands.

It was the women's job to dismantle the tepees, bind the lodge poles together with rawhide strips, and pack the families' belongings onto the horses and travois. It was astounding at what speed and efficiency they accomplished these tasks.

In the meantime, the men attended to their weapons and readied their horses for traveling. Since the warriors were the protectors of the women and children it was their responsibility to ride in the front of the procession, checking for possible danger from enemy tribes or from the *wasicus*, an even greater threat. Younger warriors were chosen to take up the rear and sound the alarm in the event of an attack from behind.

The traveling bands started forth just after sunrise. Heavy rains pelted them from the start, crackling against their skin like a hive of angry bees. To make matters worse the wind lashed out with a vengeance, slowing progress almost to a crawl.

Dakota shivered beneath his buffalo robe, now

heavy and wet from the unmerciful rain. He was cold and miserable, longing for the comfort of his own bed, a cup of hot chocolate, and maybe even a game of chess with Jon-Jay. He had yet to beat him at the game, but he was beginning to understand what his grandfather often repeated to him: "Be patient and plan your strategy before venturing out."

He peered inside his robe at the blackbird, snuggled warmly in an open drum Sitting Bull had made for it, its wing set in buffalo sticks and wrapped in soft strips of deer hide. The bird was growing stronger thanks to the chief's medicine. Soon the wing would heal, much like Dakota's shoulder, and the blackbird would be ready to take flight, perhaps to help guide him home.

A powerful gust of wind drove straight into Dakota, making his eyes water and slowing his progress. He couldn't understand why Peeshkoh and the other Hunkpapas seemed so unaffected by the elements. When Dakota had complained about the blasted rain, Peeshkoh had merely shrugged and said, "The rain will stop when it is ready to. In the meantime it offers nourishment and life to *Maka*, our Mother Earth."

Even when the rain turned to hail and assaulted them like bullets, Peeshkoh did not let it interfere with their first lesson in Lakota. He moved his mount closer to Dakota's and spoke loudly enough to compete with the elements. He began by explaining that the Sioux usually greeted one another by saying *"Hau,"* which means "I am listening."

"*Hau*," repeated Dakota.

Peeshkoh went on to explain that good-byes were rarely spoken as it was believed that everyone would see each other again, if not in this life, then certainly in the afterlife. "Farewells are expressed by saying, '*Ake wancinyankin ktelo*,' 'Until I see you again.'"

Dakota repeated the words slowly, "Ah-KAY wah-CHEE-yah-kee k'TAY loh." He smiled at the way the sounds rolled off his tongue.

Dakota also learned that "yes" is "*han*," and "no" is "*hiya*."

"What is the word for 'coal?'" Dakota asked suddenly. It was what he wanted to call the black pony.

Peeshkoh thought for a moment. "*Cahli.*"

"*Cahli*," repeated Dakota, liking the way the sound lifted like the cry of a hawk. "I will name my horse 'Cahli,'" he declared, giving the mare a loving pat on the side of her neck.

Dakota repeated the new words over and over, eager to learn as much as possible. He wanted to thank Sitting Bull for all he had done for him.

A spray of rain whipped across Dakota's face, coating his eyes in mist. He shivered, not so much from cold but from what Peeshkoh had told him earlier that morning, when they were hitching the travois to the horses. Peeshkoh had been beside himself with joy, confiding to Dakota that there was going to be a great celebration that night, and both he and Dakota would be part of it. It had to do with them counting coup—with them stealing the horses from the Crows.

Dakota wiped his face with the back of his hand. Thinking about the celebration stirred something deep inside of him. It was a warm and gutsy feeling, swelling until he wanted to hoot and holler. Peeshkoh had also said that Sitting Bull was going to give him a new name—a Lakota name. Dakota decided it wouldn't hurt to stay a few more days with the Hunkpapas. He couldn't run off the day after the ceremony. Besides, his mother would be happy when she learned of all that had happened to him, how he had counted coup, killed a buffalo, and acquired a new name chosen by Sitting Bull.

Peeshkoh leaned over and gave Dakota a solid punch on his shoulder. Dakota jerked forward and grabbed a handful of Cahli's mane. "What are you thinking about?" Peeshkoh demanded.

Dakota hesitated a moment, not sure what to say. "I was thinking about tonight. What am I supposed to do anyway?"

Peeshkoh sat tall on his mount as he spoke with assurance. "When you go into the circle, do not speak. You must show the others how you counted coup by acting out to them exactly what happened."

Peeshkoh must have noticed Dakota's uncertainty, for he quickly added, "Think about how you took the Crows' horses from underneath their noses, how you knocked that boy out. Try to imagine that you are doing it all over again, only add some life to your story." Peeshkoh's smile was secretive, drawing Dakota closer into a friendship like he had never experienced before.

"You will get through it my friend, my *kola*," said Peeshkoh, his face glistening with droplets of rain.

Dakota felt heat on his face. "It's a bit scary, don't you think?" he asked, hoping Peeshkoh shared a little of his apprehension.

"*Aiii!*" exclaimed Peeshkoh, biting down on his lip. "I'd rather be wrapped in the arms of a grizzly bear."

"But, you've done this—." Dakota stopped mid-sentence, realizing that Peeshkoh was making fun of him. "It's nothing more than another eagle feather to add to your collection."

"It is much more than that!" Peeshkoh cried, his voice ringing with indignation. "It is another step closer to the position I will one day hold among my people." Peeshkoh held his head high, and with the ease of one sure of himself he galloped off and joined Tahteh and another boy who rode in front of them.

Left alone at the back of the line, Dakota wrestled with the familiar feeling of being trapped within a small space, the stifling air choking him. He had an overwhelming desire to knock Peeshkoh off his horse and ram his face into the slosh and mud and tell him that he wasn't such a big shot after all. Who did he think he was, riding off and leaving him alone like that!

Soaked to the skin, weary, and frustrated, Dakota stifled a sob that was difficult to hold down. He thought of Jon-Jay at home, milking the cows in the misty gray of morning, pulling and squeezing with his wrinkled hands over a pail of steaming milk. "It wouldn't be so bad," he thought, "to spend another

summer with my grandfather. After all, Jon-Jay had promised to take me on my first cattle drive to Lewistown at the close of the summer. He had told me it was a job worthy of a man, for one who knew his horse and the land like the back of his hand."

It had taken the long procession most of the day to travel twelve miles to the mouth of Muddy Creek. Here they set up their new camp. Despite the persistent rain and wind, the women unloaded the drenched horses and travois with the same efficiency that they showed that morning. Soon they had the lodges assembled, beds made, and fires burning a warm welcome, the orange lights within the tepees casting a transparent glow throughout the camp.

As Dakota was leading Cahli into the pony corral, a long shadow crossed in front of him. He looked up and saw a warrior mounted on a fine buckskin horse cross in front of him. Their eyes met for a fleeting moment. In that second Dakota could feel the heat of passion behind the warrior's eyes. It was as if the man were looking right through him, seeing something that nobody else could see.

Peeshkoh came up behind Dakota and whispered, "They call him 'The Strange One,' that Crazy Horse."

"Crazy Horse!" Dakota cried, staring at the warrior with even greater interest.

"He doesn't speak much or participate in any of

the ceremonies," continued Peeshkoh, rolling his eyes in disgust. "He is happy when he has only himself for company."

"There's nothing wrong with that!" Dakota fired back. "Crazy Horse is a legend. There will never be a warrior who will fight as well as him."

Peeshkoh studied Dakota as if they were meeting for the first time. "They should call you 'The Strange One,'" he said, pushing hard against Dakota's chest so that he stumbled and fell backward. Peeshkoh laughed and helped him back to his feet.

Dakota wasn't sure if his laughter was in jest or if it rang with an element of truth. Sometimes it was hard to read between the words Peeshkoh threw at him.

"You better go and help Toskala before she comes looking for you," teased Peeshkoh, backing away. "She might keep you from attending the ceremony—just to teach you a lesson."

Dakota nodded without responding. He was thinking about Crazy Horse. He ran his fingers through his thick hair, breaking through the matted knots. I will grow my hair long and wear it in braids like Crazy Horse, he thought. His hair is the same dark brown as mine, and his skin is just as light. These simple characteristics he shared with the legendary war chief pleased him, made him feel less of an outcast among the Sioux.

When Dakota arrived at the southern end of the village where the Hunkpapas camped, he quickly found the smaller tepee belonging to Toskala and the larger one of Sitting Bull in front, facing the river. He

crawled inside the smaller one and drew himself to his full height, telling himself to be cool in front of Toskala, to let her know that he was no longer a mere boy she could push around with endless chores.

Dakota stopped when he saw Toskala lying on her stomach on her buffalo rug, her hands tucked underneath her chest and her body rising and falling with each labored breath. Without making a sound he passed by her, thinking it strange that she was sleeping before the evening meal was prepared. Then he remembered how tired she had looked that morning, her eyes glossy and her face chalky. She had even let Dakota leave without giving him any chores to do.

"It must be my lucky day," he thought, setting the drum with the blackbird in it on his buffalo rug, then plopping down beside it.

All at once, the bird started to chirp in loud, agitated cries. At the same time Toskala started coughing so badly her frail body shook.

"Man-o-man-o-man! Now what am I supposed to do?" There was something unsettling in the way the eyes of the blackbird watched him, and something even more unsettling in the way the old woman tossed and turned so restlessly.

Dakota stripped off his wet clothes, all but his breechcloth and the beaded necklace he wore around his neck. He had made it the night before from a strip of sinew and a handful of beads Peeshkoh had given him.

He was in a hurry to help Peeshkoh erect the sweat lodge. It was necessary for them to purify mind,

body, and spirit through the intense heat and steam of the *inipi* before attending the evening ceremony. Peeshkoh had insisted it had to be done.

He dashed out of the tepee, glad to get away from the noise and his uncertainty about whether or not he should do something for Toskala. He promised himself he would check on her as soon as he returned.

The air resonated with the sounds of children laughing and shouting, dogs barking, and campfires crackling under damp buffalo chips. When Dakota reached the narrow strip of land between the village and the river, he searched up and down until he saw Peeshkoh with Sitting Bull and Pizi, all busy around an oval structure that looked like an igloo and which Peeshkoh called an *"initi."* It was made of intertwined willow branches and covered with hide robes. From its flap door, a narrow path had been cleared and led to a small pit only a few yards away. An older man stood over a burning fire, tending red-hot rocks with the end of a stick.

Dakota halted in front of the others, short-winded and flushed by a measure of guilt at having left Toskala. The others were already rubbing sage and sweet grass all over their bodies, not one of them bothering to say a word to Dakota.

Dakota grabbed a handful of the sage and did as Peeshkoh, first rubbing the soft silvery green leaves over his face, then behind his neck. The sage was sharp and sweet, making his skin tingle with freshness, the way it did after a long, soapy bath. He mixed some

sweet grass with the sage and rubbed it vigorously against his skin, working the scant moisture from the leaves over his chest and arms.

As Dakota bent down to rub the sage along his feet, he caught sight of Sitting Bull as he was entering the sweat lodge with his pipe, only to return moments later and follow the narrow path to the mound of earth. Here, the chief proceeded to place his pipe so that the stem faced eastward.

As the chief turned toward the sweat lodge, Peeshkoh signaled for Dakota to follow and they all entered the *initi*, circling sunwise around a shallow hole that was lined with pine needles and sitting down on a blanket of sage.

Peeshkoh bent close to Dakota and nodded toward the pit. "It is the center of the universe—the place where Great Spirit dwells," he whispered.

A stillness followed, breathless and solemn as the old man passed Sitting Bull's pipe into the lodge and both chiefs and Peeshkoh smoked from it, each taking time to offer a short prayer to *Wakan Tanka*.

When they were finished the old man passed four red-hot stones to the shallow pit, then closed the flap door, throwing everything into darkness. Sitting Bull tossed a cup of water onto the stones, making them hiss and pop like gunfire.

Three times Pizi opened the flap door to relieve their sweltering bodies, and each time he closed it Sitting Bull tossed more water onto the stones, filling the lodge with steamy clouds. Dakota felt his skin turn

wet and slippery like that of a trout. Sweat trickled down the sides of his face and down his back. He lowered his head between his legs to lessen the intensity of the heat. His head lolled from side to side, empty of all thoughts, but with the sense that he was floating away from himself.

When the heat became nearly unbearable, the old man opened the flap door a final time, and they all crawled out and headed for the river. Dakota's feet skipped and sloshed through the mud, kicking up clumps of dirt and grass as he ran. At the river he plunged headfirst into the water, letting the cold cut through him like a steel blade. As he sank deeper and deeper, the water became cooler and more velvety against his skin. He closed his eyes against the murky shadows, rolling his body into a tight ball and letting himself spin faster and faster through the water, only one thought on his mind—receiving a new name, a Lakota name—a name chosen by Sitting Bull. His heart soared like an eagle.

When Dakota returned to his tepee, he found Toskala the same as he had left her, only now she was curled in a ball, one side of her face exposed like a half-moon, stale and colorless. He tiptoed past her, then stopped and listened. Her breathing was more pronounced, more disturbing. He kneeled beside her and leaned close enough to feel her hot breath on his face. Strands of black and gray hair clung to her with-

ered skin like salamanders. He thought she could be at least a hundred years old.

Dakota touched Toskala on her shoulder, then drew his hand away, surprised at how hot her flesh was. He tried once again to rouse her, his fingers pressing into the bony flesh of her shoulder, shaking her harder as he spoke her name. In the background, the blackbird chirped wildly, its cries carrying a note of alarm that made Dakota feel cold inside and out.

Toskala stirred slightly, then lifted her face to Dakota for a twinkling of a second and murmured a single word, "Mni."

He scrambled to his feet. "Of course!" he cried. "Water. That's what she wants." He found a container and raced to the river with it wrapped securely in his arms. Filling it only halfway, he hurried back.

Dakota found a buffalo horn and dipped it in the water. He nudged Toskala lightly on her shoulder and said, "Mni."

Toskala raised her head and tried to take the buffalo horn from Dakota, but her hand was shaking and she could barely hold her head up. He placed his hand behind her neck and held the cup to her lips, letting her drink as much as she wanted.

"Pilamaya," Toskala whispered, her eyes reflecting a gentleness Dakota had not seen before.

He sat next to her, not sure what to do. He wished Peeshkoh was nearby so he could take the matter in his own hands. He remembered how his mother would place cold towels on his forehead and neck whenever he had a fever. "It probably wouldn't

hurt," he thought, getting up reluctantly and searching for a cloth.

Dakota dunked his T-shirt into the water and wrung it out with both hands. Toskala was still lying on her back, her eyes closed and her chest rising and falling. He held the T-shirt above her face and hesitated. A drop of water splashed against her eyelash, causing it to flutter. He laid the cloth across her forehead, then backed away. He wanted to get Peeshkoh, but the realization that Sitting Bull was much closer and Toskala needed immediate help made him reconsider.

Dakota left Toskala and stopped in front of Sitting Bull's lodge, the thought of turning back heavy on his mind. He found himself wishing once again he were back in Roundup where life was simple and more predictable. This kind of life was going to make him older than Jon-Jay if he wasn't careful.

All at once, two young boys came bursting out of Sitting Bull's tepee, almost knocking Dakota over. He steadied himself by grabbing the shoulders of one of the boys. He looked down at him, not knowing what to say. The boy pulled away and planted himself in front of Dakota with his arms crossed over his chest.

"Tatanka Iyotanka? Is he here?" Dakota asked, his voice sharp with the urgency of his calling.

The boys looked at each other, then ran back inside. In only a matter of seconds, Sitting Bull was outside, towering over Dakota, his bare chest swimming in front of him like a black sea.

Dakota pointed to the tepee behind Sitting Bull's and said, "Toskala!"

Sitting Bull left Dakota and disappeared into Toskala's tepee. Dakota waited outside until Sitting Bull reemerged, only to return once again with one of his wives and his arms full of what Dakota guessed was the chief's medicine.

Feeling out of place, Dakota went to the river and dug for worms for the blackbird. The sun had already slipped to the edge of the mountains, painting the sky in sheets of orange and rose, the same color as his collie Sierra. He wished his dog was with him now. He would have liked to wrap his arms around her thick neck and feel the warmth of her soft breathing against his face.

For whatever reason, the earlier excitement Dakota had felt about the ceremony began to fade with the setting sun. The more he thought about it, the crazier it all seemed. He couldn't imagine himself at the center of the circle, with hundreds of Sioux and Cheyenne watching him as he stumbled through a performance he had no idea how to begin or end.

Then an idea took hold of him, freeing his mind of dread and reminding him of his intent. "This is the perfect time to slip away," he reasoned, "while everyone is busy preparing for the festivities."

CHAPTER 8

Wahpa Tanka Newne

Eager to retrieve his belongings, Dakota pushed through the door of his tepee and slammed against Many Horses, nearly knocking her over. He tried to catch her, forgetting that the turtle shell bowl he carried was full of worms, and ended up spilling them down her chest and all over her feet.

Many Horses backed away, her eyes wide. She looked down at her bare feet and watched the worms crawling all over them. A smile spread across her face, which she quickly covered with her hand. Her muffled giggling filled the spaces between their silence and somewhat eased Dakota's horror.

Dropping to his hands and knees, he brushed and scooped and plucked every worm that crawled and wiggled over her feet, repeating over and over again, "I'm really sorry, I'm really sorry." When Dakota stood, he noted with surprise that she was carrying the drum, the blackbird peeking over the rim. He quickly dumped the worms inside, one thought searing through his brain: "I'm such an idiot!"

Many Horses twisted the drum in her hands, her

face strained with the effort of keeping a straight face. Toskala was also smiling from her bed, a blanket wrapped around her shoulders and a buffalo rug on her lap. She signaled Dakota to come forward. He hesitated, wondering what she wanted. Did she have more work for him the moment he was alone with Many Horses, the moment he should be planning his escape?

Toskala pulled something from under her buffalo rug and handed it to Dakota. It was a pair of black leggings, decorated with hundreds of colorful beads and long fringes that ran along the outside of either leg.

Dakota was speechless. It was obvious that Toskala had spent many hours working on this. Was she giving it to him? He turned the leggings over and studied the intricate details of her beadwork. Every line and pattern was perfect. At the bottom of one of the legs he noticed two small horse hooves. Did they represent the horses he had taken from the Crows? He gazed up at Toskala. "Is this for . . . me?"

The old woman coughed and wheezed and shooed Dakota away with a swish of her hand. As she sank back into her bed, he noticed her face was filmy gray and her lips cracked and dry.

"*Pilamaya*," Dakota said softly, remembering the words for "thank you."

Toskala nodded her approval before closing her eyes, obviously pleased with his first use of Lakota with her.

Dakota turned to Many Horses, not knowing what to do. Only moments ago he had resolved to

find his way back home. Now he was face to face with Sitting Bull's daughter, who currently had possession of his bird, while he held a pair of leggings meant to be worn at the upcoming ceremony.

Many Horses waved to Dakota to follow her, and he gladly did so, his footsteps swift and eager, and his expectations rising even faster.

She took him to the rear of her father's large tepee where his buffalo rug was already spread out. On top of it lay a beautiful shirt he had never seen before. Many Horses handed the drum to Dakota and waited quietly by his side.

He stared at the ceremonial shirt that was spread like a cross, beaded bands running all the way down the shoulders and arms. He lifted it over his head and let it fall over his chest like a poncho, covering his hips. "Incredible!" he said, admiring the soft blue that circled around the bottom like the sky, and the upper half radiating the brilliance of the sun.

Soft footsteps swished behind him. Dakota swung around and observed Four Robes coming toward him. She handed two turtle shell bowls to Many Horses, then patted the floor, indicating to Dakota to sit. He did as he was told, eyeing Many Horses as she set the bowls in front of him and took a seat nearby.

Four Robes ran her fingers through one of the bowls. When she drew them out they were thick with black paint. She rubbed the cool substance across Dakota's forehead and down his cheeks. He closed his

eyes as her fingers made gentle lines and circles on his face.

When he opened his eyes he noticed that Sitting Bull and his older wife, Seen-by-the-Nation, had returned. The chief's wife was busy attending to her husband, her hands moving with expert care as she braided his hair and wrapped it in otter fur. Sitting Bull smiled at her with a spark of appreciation lighting up his dark eyes. Dakota remembered only a few such moments passing between his parents, and that was many years ago.

When Four Robes was finished, she smiled and handed Dakota a small looking glass. He hesitated, almost reluctant to confront his image in the mirror. He brought the glass slowly to his face then drew it back, startled. It was as if he were looking at Peeshkoh on the day he had first encountered him.

"Whoa!" he cried, bringing the glass back to his face. His eyes were brighter and clearer, and he thought he looked less wimpy, his features hinting at a firmness that would one day replace his boyish face. He ran a finger along the scar that formed an "S" along his left cheek, a reminder of his perilous crossing of the Little Bighorn River.

Dakota handed the mirror back to Four Robes and ran his hand over the beaded band of his shirt sleeve. He wondered why everyone was treating him with such kindness, as if he were a member of their family. What had he done to deserve such treatment?

Four Robes gathered together her bowls and

brushes and got up to leave. Dakota noticed that Sitting Bull and Seen-by-the-Nation had already left. He leaped to his feet and offered his hand to Many Horses, but she ignored his gesture and rose on her own. Only a few feet separated them. Dakota side-stepped into her path and gave her his most winning smile.

Many Horses surprised him by passing so close to him that her hair brushed against his cheek. She glanced over her shoulder and smiled back.

For a brief moment, Dakota thought he smelled honeysuckle in the air. His heart swelled, then tightened, throwing him off balance. He watched her leave, marveling that he had never seen a girl as pretty as Sitting Bull's daughter.

Dakota tried to steady himself. "Whoa!" He clenched his fists, feeling wild and reckless as his feet danced around the tepee, filling him with such joy it left him breathless. Suddenly, he froze, aware that someone had reentered the tepee. He spun around and came face to face with Sitting Bull. He let his arms fall to his sides and clapped his legs together like a soldier at attention. He prayed that Sitting Bull had not understood the reason behind his sudden madness.

The chief shook his head at Dakota and said, "Witko," but Dakota could tell by the gleam in his eyes and the way the corner of his mouth curled up that Sitting Bull was in good spirits. For now, his secret was safe.

Dakota stepped back and admired the figure before him. The pictures he had seen in books didn't

do justice to the warrior before him. Sitting Bull was attired in a magnificent war shirt that was heavily beaded in green, yellow, blue, and red. Around his neck was a string of grizzly bear claws that were attached to an otter skin. What particularly struck Dakota as beautiful was the eagle-feather headdress that flowed down the chief's back, reaching all the way to the ground.

Sitting Bull made small circles in the air with his finger, signaling Dakota to turn around. Dakota did what he was told and felt something heavy slip over his neck and shoulders. He looked down at his chest and gasped. It was a hair-pipe bone breast plate, a traditional ornament worn during ceremonial dances. At least thirty rows of brass beads covered his chest. Black horsehair dangled from the bottom, looking like miniature scalps. He had seen breast plates similar to this at the Sioux museum in Rapid City. Today he would have the honor of wearing one to the ceremony that would bring him one step closer to manhood.

Outside, the steady rumble of drums grew louder and more pronounced. Dakota rubbed his sweaty palms together and took a deep breath. There was no turning back, even though his head was swimming with doubt and his legs were too heavy to move. As if aware of his discomfort, Sitting Bull laid his hand on Dakota's shoulder and led him toward the circle of dancers.

Dakota found Peeshkoh right away. He was standing outside the circle watching the dancers and musicians get ready. Like Dakota, he too was wearing

magnificent clothes worthy of a warrior. Black and red paint covered his face, with a yellow circle drawn around his left eye, giving him the look of a wild animal. The two boys exchanged nervous grins, each trying to show the other that he was unaffected by the events that were about to take place.

A restless wind kicked through the village, flattening the prairie grass and causing the tepee poles to rattle. It made the huge bonfire flash streaks of gold all around. Willow and sage bundles crackled, filling the evening with an earthy fragrance. Sensations swirled around Dakota like a dream, spinning him into a cloud of intoxication.

At the southern opening of the circle, a procession of dancers moved sunwise around the fire. At least two hundred men and women joined hands, forming a large circle. Their brightly colored costumes and jewelry swished and jangled to the uniform beat of the drums and the soft serenade of the flutes.

A strong hand pushed Dakota from behind, forcing him toward the center. On the other side of the circle, he caught sight of Peeshkoh hunched over like a fox stalking its pray, his clothes twirling outward as he danced around the fire, acting out his coup.

Dakota shut his eyes, letting the sound of the drum roll into him, hearing it beat like his heart, fast and furiously. His mind journeyed back to the raid against the Crows. He let himself act out the part where he crept close to the enemy's camp and dismounted. On his hands and knees Dakota crawled forward, then rose, showing the others how he had

cut the horses loose with the slash of his knife. He peered behind him and from side to side, watching for the enemy.

Dakota hesitated a moment, scanning the faces of a group of warriors who stood beyond the circle of dancers, waving their coup sticks as they cheered him. This was new to him, to be encouraged like that, especially by boys older than himself. He fell backward, hitting the ground hard as he thrashed out at the person on top of him. For a moment he imagined that it was his father wrestling with him, the way he used to, a long time ago.

His muscles tightened at the memory, ready to burst. Falling to his side, Dakota rolled across the dirt in a tight ball, at the same time reaching for a rock. He lifted his arm high above his head but faltered for a second, unsure of what he was doing. An image of his father in his new home in Alaska, with his new wife and his new baby, flashed before him. Little Jonathan Jason Miles, only nine months old and named after his grandfather, Jon-Jay. Dakota blinked several times, then let his hand slam downward, smashing the image that had sent a pain searing through his chest. Again and again Dakota raised his arm and brought it down, the edge of the rock cutting across the ground—swish, swish. "You are a bastard, Travis Miles!" he cried. "You have ruined my mother's life!"

The drumbeat quickened, reaching a crescendo. Dakota dropped his head between his legs and breathed deeply. The weight of the last two years dissolved like particles of snow at his feet. He raised his

head and felt the wind of a hundred dancers circling around him, their feet pounding the ground, making it shake.

From the southern end of the circle two women came forward, each carrying her husband's coup stick. On the end of each pole dangled the scalps that were taken from their enemies, the Crows. The women chanted and danced in small circles, parading their husbands' trophies high above their heads.

As soon as Dakota found an opportunity he slipped between two dancers and joined the others on the outside. He watched the circle of dancers with renewed spirits. "They are truly a happy people," he thought. All around him Sitting Bull's followers sang and danced with a joy he had never seen before. It is a good day to be alive, he thought, embracing the fervor that exploded like fireworks all around him.

Dakota wanted to find Sitting Bull, to tell him how happy he felt at this very moment, how he had never experienced such joy, ever. He was weightless, a burden lifted and freed. Tearing past the throngs of people, he searched for the person wearing the magnificent headdress. Finally, he saw him, leaning against a cottonwood tree, alone and pensive. He ran forward, then stopped abruptly. "What if he wants to be alone?" he wondered. As he started to leave, Sitting Bull waved to him.

Dakota raced forward, feeling as if he could take flight like a bird and soar beyond the heavens. He stopped, breathless and a little unsure, in front of Sitting Bull. Sitting Bull ran his hand gently over the

top of his hair. He fell against the chief, burying his face against his chest, swallowing a sob. He couldn't help himself. He couldn't pull himself away. Sitting Bull didn't seem to mind. He just continued stroking his hair.

The preparation for the *hunka* ceremony didn't begin until the sun began to descend and the shadows of evening danced across the darkening plains. Only hours before the ceremony Peeshkoh had taken Dakota aside and explained in great detail what was expected of him, the significance of each segment of the ritual, how it would bind him to Sitting Bull as closely as if they were bound by blood.

After Dakota and Sitting Bull stripped down to their breechcloths, leggings, and moccasins, they stepped out of the preparation lodge and were met by the *wicasa wakan* of the Hunkpapas. He led Dakota and Sitting Bull to the ceremonial lodge, a large structure prepared that morning by the women. A gathering of chosen guests, all singing a song, followed the *hunka* participants. Dakota smiled broadly when he caught sight of Peeshkoh and Pizi, as well as Many Horses and other members of Sitting Bull's family.

The *wicasa wakan* led Dakota and Sitting Bull to the rear of the lodge where they took seats on the sage that covered the ground. Between the place of honor and the fireplace the altar was arranged. On one end stood a large rock and on the other the skull

of a buffalo. Between the two was a scaffold that held the choice meat of a buffalo.

Dakota sat tall and watched spellbound as the *wicasa wakan* handed one of the helpers a square rod of red cedar about eight feet long and as thick as his thumb. Jumping Bull, the adopted brother of Sitting Bull, and One Bull were each handed a wand that was painted red and adorned with quills from the tail of a golden eagle and tufts from the tail of a horse. Next, the *wicasa wakan* handed a fire stick to Pizi and rattles painted red with blue stripes to Peeshkoh and Tahteh.

A stillness settled like nightfall. The *wicasa wakan* prepared his ceremonial pipe while Pizi used the fire stick to carry four burning coals to the altar. Once the spirit fire was ready, Pizi took the fire stick to the *wicasa wakan*, who lit his pipe from the burning coals.

While the *wicasa wakan* smoked, Pizi arranged the buffalo meat on the scaffold, carefully separating the fat from the lean meat. The *wicasa wakan* joined Pizi at the scaffold and began sprinkling a ceremonial herb over the meat, speaking a few sacred words as he did this. He then handed Pizi some sweetgrass, which he sprinkled over the fire, filling the inside of the tepee with a pleasing aroma.

In the slow and quiet manner of the elders, the *wicasa wakan* walked to the door of the lodge, raised the mouthpiece of the pipe toward the sky, and said, "*Mihunka*, we bring you a nephew today."

Once again Pizi sprinkled sweetgrass over the fire. As the smoke and incense rose the *wicasa wakan* turned to Dakota and said in a thunderous voice, "I will make

you a *hunka* and I will teach you how to live as one."

Sweat trickled down Dakota's temples as an icy chill raced through his body. One by one, Pizi, Jumping Bull, One Bull, and other members of Sitting Bull's tribe stepped forward and addressed the *hunka* participants, advising them of the honor and obligation of the *hunka* to be industrious, generous, brave, and honest.

A great feast followed, with each guest and participant receiving a portion of the meat as a demonstration of generosity and charity. Numerous gifts were exchanged, with Sitting Bull giving away many of his horses and fine animal skins.

When the feast drew to a close, Sitting Bull led Dakota to the center of the tepee, close to the fire. He handed him the drum that held the blackbird. Dakota saw something whimsical flash across the chief's face. Peering into the drum, he saw that the bandages had been removed from the broken wing. A joyful chirp rose from the drum, silencing the room. Sitting Bull turned to the others and said a few words lost to Dakota.

Everyone was nodding and smiling, all but Dakota, who turned to Peeshkoh for help. His friend grinned. "Tatanka Iyotanka said, 'The blackbird will not fly without you. Let us hope that the boy will stay until he can see with his heart, until he knows what it is that holds our people together, as firmly as a tree rooted to the ground.'"

Sitting Bull spoke again, his words coming slowly, as if he were considering each thought carefully. They were words that Dakota could not understand, but

words he could feel, like the sun warming his face. Sitting Bull laid his hand on his shoulder and said, "Wahpa Tanka Newne." The words sounded like the wind breathing through the canyons.

Peeshkoh slapped Dakota on his back. "Well, my *kola*, my friend, you have a new name."

"What is it?" he asked. "What is my new name?"

Peeshkoh leaned forward and whispered the words, stressing each syllable, "Wah-pa Tan-ka New-ne." He winked at Dakota. "You are now Lost Blackbird."

Dakota repeated his new name, "Wahpa Tanka Newne." He took the blackbird out of the drum and rubbed its feathers against his cheek. "It has a nice ring to it, don't you think?"

The blackbird cocked its head to one side and chirped loudly, "Konk-la-ree, konk-la-ree."

CHAPTER 9

Bear Tracks

After three days of heavy rains that widened the mouth of Muddy Creek and sent the river surging past them, the village collected its belongings and set off in a southwesterly direction along the Rosebud. It was mid-June, the Moon of the Chokecherries, a warm and cloudless day filled with promise. Streaks of green and gold spread out as far as the eye could see, speckled with the tiny pink and white rosebuds that had appeared late that year.

Young warriors raced their ponies up and down the three-mile procession, showing off to the young girls, who wore deerskin dresses decorated with beads the colors of a rainbow. The dogs and horses romped on either side of the travelers, kicking up dust and loose prairie grass as they bayed and barked, setting riot to the hushed prairies with the same mood of exhilaration.

Birds darted among the ponderosa pines, singing songs of celebration. Sitting Bull sang a song that Peeshkoh told Dakota the chief had composed when

he was only seventeen winters, in honor of a wood-pecker that had warned him of an approaching griz-zly bear:

Pretty bird, you saw me and took pity on me:
You wish me to survive among the people.
O Bird People, from this day always
    you shall be my relative.

Never before had the Sioux gathered so many bands together at one time. Sitting Bull had convinced his people that they were better off in numbers now that the *wasicu* was on the warpath, attacking villages indiscriminately. It did not matter if the band was considered friendly or hostile: An Indian was an Indian, and now that the snows had melted many of the Indians living on the reservations were eager to join Sitting Bull's village for the summer hunt and celebrations.

The Cheyenne located an ideal campsite at the upper fork of Sundance Creek, with a plentiful supply of firewood and grazing grass for the pony herd. Scouts, who had been sent far ahead of the procession, came galloping back, proclaiming they had sighted buffalo and large herds of elk headed for the thick timber. A buzz of excitement spread among the warriors and young boys at the expectation of a good hunt.

By late afternoon, many of the warriors surrendered to the lazy heat of midday, napping either in their tepees or underneath the shade of a nearby cottonwood tree. At the chief's lodge, Sitting Bull pushed

everyone out into the sunshine, claiming that he needed sleep and quiet.

Dakota was glad to be outside. He loved the feel of the sun drawing out the sweat that slid down his skin, igniting a desire to do something reckless. He found Peeshkoh and Tahteh leaning against a willow tree, their arrows spread around them like buffalo bones discarded after a feast. Dakota threw his quiver and bow to the ground and greeted the boys with a simple *"Hau."* When neither boy responded, Dakota pulled a straightening stone from his quiver and began sharpening his arrowheads, wondering whether or not Peeshkoh would accept his company now that his friend Tahteh was present.

Peeshkoh eventually broke the silence by signaling with a nod of his head at Tahteh. "He wants to know why you do not speak Lakota since you have Indian blood in you." This same question must have been brooding inside of Peeshkoh, for he added with a sharpness in his voice, "Why did your mother not teach you her tongue?"

Dakota stared at them with a blank face. What kind of answer could he give without them thinking he was crazy? He thought about the time his father had joined Savannah and him on a visit to the Standing Rock Reservation in South Dakota, how his father kept insisting that the Indians needed to forget their past and move forward if they wanted to prosper and live decent lives. Savannah's face had twisted in anger as she lunged at his father, shouting in his face, "It will

take more than a lifetime to forget our past! The old ways are still in our blood!"

"My father is a white man," Dakota blurted out. "He didn't let my mother speak Lakota in our house." Dakota kicked at the dirt. "He thinks that the Indians drink too much and don't work hard enough."

Peeshkoh sneered in disgust, then translated for Tahteh. He then turned to Dakota and said, "The *wasicus* are all alike, *witko*, crazy! They bring whiskey to our village and force us to live on reservations. What kind of work can we do on a small piece of land? We must hunt to feed our people, to make our lodges and clothe our people!"

Dakota didn't know what to say. He was angry at his father, but he didn't like Peeshkoh calling him crazy.

Before any of them knew it, Peeshkoh was speaking Lakota, then English at such a rate that he finally threw his hands up in exasperation and cried, "You two had better learn to speak to each other or be prepared to pay me back with many horses."

Dakota and Tahteh agreed, telling Peeshkoh they would join the next raid and steal plenty, no matter what.

Peeshkoh stirred restlessly, swatting at the summer flies that buzzed noisily around his face. "We should test the strength of our arrows in a contest," he suggested.

Dakota and Tahteh looked at each other and shrugged. Tahteh rose and stretched his bony arms and legs and spoke to Peeshkoh, his eyes bright with

excitement. Peeshkoh translated for Dakota, telling him that Tahteh wanted to make a wager.

Dakota adjusted his quiver so it fell over his shoulder, not saying a word. Making a wager of any kind didn't set well with him. He wasn't secure enough with his arrow shooting, nor did he have anything to gamble.

Tahteh wasn't about to let the opportunity of a good bet slip away. He asked Peeshkoh what he wanted to wager.

Peeshkoh let his eyes wander toward the mountains. He was quiet, giving the question some thought. He turned and looked hard at Dakota. "I was thinking we could each put up a horse."

Dakota frowned. "I don't have an extra horse."

"What do you mean?" snapped Peeshkoh. "You have the gray mare."

Dakota shuffled the dirt in front of him with the tip of his moccasin. "That mare is for Sitting Bull," he said, his voice crackling in response to the tension he observed on his friend's face.

"Tatanka Iyotanka!" exclaimed Peeshkoh. "What does he need more horses for? Have you given it to him already?"

Dakota hesitated. "Not yet, but I was going to offer the mare to him tonight." He started to give his friend an explanation but thought better of it.

"Humph," scoffed Peeshkoh. "I think you should return to Toskala and begin preparing the winter coats."

Tahteh spoke up in a loud and excited voice.

"Waste," said Peeshkoh, smiling at Dakota. "Tahteh said he will wager his pinto—a good, fast pony. I will wager the white stallion." He grinned at Dakota. "Why not try and win the stallion back? It would be a fine gift for Many Horses," he teased.

Dakota didn't know what to say to Peeshkoh. If he didn't agree to participate in the contest, then he would be left behind.

"All right, Peeshkoh," he said, trying to calm the edge in his voice. "I'll bet the gray mare."

Peeshkoh slapped Dakota on the back, telling him he was a good friend to have around.

"Yeah, right," mumbled Dakota. "An idiot! That's what I am."

At the pony corral, Dakota broke away from the others in search of Cahli, glad that the black pony wasn't part of the bet. Once they were mounted, the three headed in the direction of the Wolf Mountains. When they reached the mountains' edge, Peeshkoh halted his pony and dismounted. "This is a good place to hunt," he said.

In front of them tall elm and pine trees stood as thick as quills on the back of a porcupine, with patches of sagebrush growing in twisted knots around their feet, shielding the wildflowers that rose in glorious clusters.

Before they began, Peeshkoh retold a story that Sitting Bull had told him of the time when Tatanka Iyotanka was only ten winters old. The great arrow maker, Village Center, organized a contest in which he offered a bow and a set of arrows to the boy who

could shoot the prettiest bird from a tree. When the boys spread their trophies in front of Village Center he chose the prettiest bird and offered it as a sacrifice to Wakan Tanka.

"Who won the contest?" asked Dakota, certain of the answer before it was given.

"At that time," said Peeshkoh, "Tatanka Iyotanka was known as Slow. He never got a chance to shoot a bird, but he won the contest."

Dakota raised his eyebrows. "How did he pull that off?" he asked.

"There was a boy who shot his favorite arrow into an oak tree and the shaft got caught between some branches," continued Peeshkoh. "He was so frustrated that he offered his finest arrow to anyone who could dislodge it. When it was Slow's turn, he shot the arrow out of the tree, but at the same time he shattered it. The boy became very angry and demanded that Slow pay for the damage he had done. Slow did not want a quarrel to break out, so he gave his arrow to the boy, saying, 'Keep it and get your bird.' When the birds were all laid out in front of Village Center," continued Peeshkoh, "a boy came forward and told of how Slow had ended the quarrel by giving his prize arrow to the boy whose arrow he had shattered. All agreed that Slow had shown himself a man that day and he should be awarded the prize."

Dakota smiled to himself. It was good to know that Sitting Bull had not killed a bird and still managed to win the contest.

"We will shoot six of our finest arrows," Peeshkoh

instructed. "Any birds we drop from the trees will be taken to Tatanka Iyotanka. He will decide which is the prettiest."

Dakota and Tahteh both agreed that Tatanka Iyotanka would be a fair judge.

After Dakota had selected six arrows he glanced sideways at Tahteh, who was rocking back and forth with nervous energy. "He is impatient to get started," thought Dakota. "He is confident he will win."

"Hoppo," called Peeshkoh, swinging to the left and creeping along the edge of the woods, his arrow set on his bow.

Dakota watched the others move quietly among the trees. He felt something heavy sink deep into the pit of his stomach. Thinking about the birds brought their full chorus to his ears, making the weight inside him feel more uncertain. He had never shot a bird before—never had the desire. He thought of his blackbird safe in Sitting Bull's tepee. It didn't make any sense that he had saved the blackbird and now he was scouting the woods for the most beautiful bird he could kill.

Moving with slow, deliberate steps, Dakota listened to the merry trilling that called to him from every direction. His eyes followed the sounds of a shrill chirrup that came from high above a pine tree. A beautiful golden-winged woodpecker looked down at him as if in greeting. He backed away from the sound, turning his eyes in another direction.

Pushing deeper into the woods, Dakota brushed away the thick foliage that slapped across his face. A

shrill noise brought him to an abrupt halt. "Chip-chiree, chip-chiree." Perched high above him was a brilliant orange oriole, its black head bobbing up and down as if it were ready to take flight. Dakota drew his bowstring back, not thinking of anything but victory. As soon as he felt the full tension in his bow, he released the string with an easy twang, sending the arrow straight at the bird. A loud swish of wings fanned above him, then shot across the sky in a ball of fire. Dakota breathed a sigh of relief as the bird disappeared from sight.

A loud cry broke from deep inside the woods. Dakota looked up to see Tahteh running toward him, whooping and hollering as he waved his arrow above his head. At the end of it dangled the limp body of a golden-winged woodpecker. Dakota's hand flew over his mouth. It was the same kind of bird that had warned Sitting Bull of the approaching grizzly bear.

Tahteh followed close behind Peeshkoh, who scowled bitterly as he heaved his way through the thick branches, searching for his lost arrow. "God damn!" he shouted, throwing his bow to the ground. "I lost my fourth arrow—my best arrow—in some damn bushes." Dakota and Tahteh couldn't help but laugh at their friend. He was steaming like a bull.

Peeshkoh waved to them to follow. "Help me find it, will you?" It was more of a command than a request.

Dakota consulted the sun. There were only a few hours of daylight left. Already the Wolf Mountains were casting long shadows all around them, drawing them into its darkness. He joined Tahteh and together

they followed Peeshkoh into the timber. Dakota shuffled behind the others, his mind racing. Now that Peeshkoh was practically eliminated, he had to find a bird prettier than the one Tahteh had found. Stealing the gray mare had almost cost him his life, and it was all he had to offer Sitting Bull to show his gratitude.

The boys reached the area where Peeshkoh's arrow had disappeared. The sagebrush was thick and dry, the ground matted with clusters of grass and moss, making it difficult to see anything. Dakota pushed forward, then stopped. A rustling sound broke into the stillness. Before he had time to consider the origin of the noise, a thunderous clap of hooves exploded all around him. Dakota jumped back in alarm. A herd of elk bolted from the timber, scurrying in all directions.

"Hai!" screamed Peeshkoh, his voice shrill with excitement. He turned to the others. "We will have a good hunt now!"

The elk were everywhere, dozens of them, grunting and bellowing as they stampeded through the woods. Branches snapped and crackled under the heavy hooves, creating chaos all around the boys. Dakota drew his breath in. This was a hunter's dream—to be at the very heart of such a herd.

Some of the elk plunged deeper into the security of the woods, while a few darted toward the open prairie. A handful of elk were so paralyzed with fear they didn't even move.

The boys fumbled for their arrows, eager to hear the twang of their bowstrings. The adrenaline charged

through Dakota, making him laugh out loud. He started pumping arrows into the massive hides as fast as he could set his bow. He couldn't believe their luck. Over two thousand warriors were sleeping the afternoon away, while the three of them were in the heart of a mighty herd.

Dakota had only two arrows left. He set his bow and aimed at a bull that was pressed against a nearby tree, its eyes glazed with terror, its mouth open, panting. The bull watched Dakota as if there were a chance he might take mercy on him. Dakota hung back for a second, struggling with a thought. He set his jaw firmly, remembering to strike behind the elk's shoulders where the lungs were. It was the vital spot his grandfather had told him to aim for, as a hit there was usually fatal and caused less suffering to the animal.

Dakota sent his arrow whizzing through the air. He closed his eyes to the sound of the arrowhead ripping through thick hide and muscle. When he opened them he saw the elk stumble forward, its forelegs crumbling like a clump of dirt in one's fist. The bull, downed by a single arrow through its lungs, hit the ground with a hard thud. Dakota figured the elk weighed at least eight hundred pounds, the antlers alone sixty.

When all of the arrows were spent the boys surveyed the carnage before them, hooting and hollering at the rewards that lay at their feet. Between them, they had killed eight bulls and two cows. Perhaps as many as five or six had escaped into the timberland, still carrying one of their arrows. Eager to get to the

wounded, the young hunters scurried here and there, retrieving arrows from the ground and yanking others from the dead carcasses.

Peeshkoh shoved his arrows into his quiver, making the trilling sound of a warrior. "*Hoppo!*" he called, waving to the others to follow. "Let's find their trail and finish them off."

Dakota felt uneasy about leaving the ones they had just killed. "What about them?" he asked, motioning toward the dark mounds all around.

"Don't worry about them," said Peeshkoh. "We cannot move them anyway. We will get help from some of the men at our village."

The boys exchanged smug looks of understanding. It was going to be a fine moment when they announced to their village that they had beat them to the herd. There would be a lot of backslapping tonight, and perhaps a little resentment as well.

Peeshkoh shuffled from side to side, trying to see through the dense trees ahead of him. When he found a narrow passageway, he called to the other two, "*Hoppo!* We will lose their trail if we do not hurry."

Dakota and Tahteh had to run to catch up to Peeshkoh as they followed him into the timberland. A misty fog was filtering through the dense foliage, cooling the air as the sun dropped and casting bars of silvery light between the trees.

Dakota drew in his chest, inhaling the earthy smells of wet grass and pinecones, savoring the peculiar sense of pride only a hunter on the trail of his prey

can understand. He had been elk hunting on a few occasions in the Musselshell Valley, but this was altogether different. Now he was sharpening his skill with the bow and arrow, a weapon requiring far more precision than a rifle.

Peeshkoh was quick to appoint himself leader, claiming he was the eldest. Neither Dakota nor Tahteh argued the matter. Peeshkoh decided that they should separate and meet at the clearing between the timber and the mountains. Dakota would circle to the right, Tahteh to the left, and Peeshkoh would forge ahead in a straight line.

"Find your blood trail," Peeshkoh called. "Let's be quick! Darkness is upon us."

Dakota felt the sharpness around him, the hunter fully aroused to every sight, sound, and smell. Squatting on his haunches he studied the ground and bushes. In front of him a trail of pink, bubbly blood had fallen in a steady line. It was the color of a lung wound. "I will find this elk and I will kill it," he told himself, the old ways of the hunter stealing into his psyche.

He followed the blood trail as it wound like a snake through narrow openings in the thicket. Dakota could tell by the distance between the tracks that the animal was slowing down. When the blood was no longer visible, he stopped and crouched behind the underbrush and listened. The elk was near, he could smell it, a unique odor, as musty and pungent as the primeval forest. He waited patiently, knowing that his

only chance at snagging the elk was to let it make the first move.

Dakota was longing to stretch his cramped legs, but still he waited, sensing the animal was nearby. The darkness was closing in fast, casting shadows of doubt. He would have to call off the hunt soon. Somewhere in the distance a wood thrush broke the silence with its series of brief, shrill calls, a reassuring sound in the isolated wilderness.

A movement, sudden and unexpected, caused Dakota to stumble and fall, scraping the side of his face on the end of a branch. He was on his feet at once, spinning around and searching the underbrush. The pungent smell of blood and sweat rushed at him, filling him with hope. The elk was close, very close.

Dakota found a narrow opening between sections of the underbrush that had been trampled. He crept forward, inching his way through the passage, listening. He hadn't gone more than twenty yards when he felt a sharp pain jab him in his thigh. Drawing back, he saw the mighty prongs of the elk sticking out of the underbrush.

The elk was lying on its side, its chest heaving up and down, desperate to get air into its shattered lungs. The first arrow had hit too high in its neck. All Dakota could think about was closing the beautiful eyes and ending the labored breathing. His bowstring twanged loudly as the arrow drove deep into the lower part of the shoulder, lower than he would have liked but still effective. The elk shuddered, then dropped its head to

the ground, closing its eyes for the last time. Dakota tried to swallow a lump that rose painfully in his throat. There had been too much killing for one day. All he wanted was to get away from the blood and death smells and return to camp where the company of Sitting Bull and Many Horses could warm a cold heart.

Dakota climbed a nearby tree and slipped an arrow between some branches, letting the feathers stick out, hoping it would serve as a reliable marker. He looked down at the elk, its body leaning against the tree, graceful even in death. He told himself it was for the good of the village—it was necessary.

It was the time of the evening meal, when the sun is ready to set. Dakota was worried about getting lost. The darkness was so close it made him feel a little tight under his belt. He pushed his way through the heavy underbrush, anxious to get to Peeshkoh's meeting place.

Dakota did not see the rotting tree trunk that was hidden beneath a pile of dead leaves and branches. He tripped and slid forward, scraping both arms and legs against some sharp thickets and stones. "Damn!" he cried, as he stood up and brushed the debris from his arms. He made a face at the blood seeping from a deep cut that jetted across the inside of his arm. He wrapped the top flap of his breechcloth around his wound and pressed hard against it.

He waited a few moments until the bleeding stopped. A few feet beyond the tree trunk he saw a strange break in the damp terrain. Peering closer,

Dakota saw what appeared to be a gigantic paw print. He wiped a line of sweat from his forehead. "Man-o-man-o-man!" It was at least a foot and a half long, and a foot wide. He searched the ground in front of him and found another imprint that was just as big.

The silence of the woods added to his uneasiness. He wrapped his arms around his chest and hurried to meet his friends, wondering what kind of bear had roamed these woods, and how long ago.

Through a clearing in the trees, Dakota heard the excited voices of Peeshkoh and Tahteh. He quickened his pace, eager to get to his friends. He wasn't sure why, but he felt pressed to get back to camp.

"*Hau,*" he called. "Any luck?"

"*Han!*" cried Peeshkoh, holding up two fingers. "Another bull and cow, each downed by a single arrow!" he said, grinning like a schoolboy.

"I got another bull," said Dakota, trying to sound more excited than he felt.

Tahteh said something to Peeshkoh, his fingers pressed against his nose and his eyes rolled back in disgust. Peeshkoh laughed hard, his lean frame bent over like a willow branch. He turned to Dakota and said, "Tahteh got nothing but a headache from keeping his nose to the ground and seeing nothing but dirt and elk *tatunkce.*"

Dakota forced a laugh. He was still thinking about the animal tracks. "We'd better get to the ponies," he said, shivering against the cool dampness that comes just before dusk.

The boys slung their quivers over their shoulders

and turned to the trail leading back to the prairie. As they stepped into the narrow passageway that would lead them back to their horses, a deafening roar stopped them in their tracks. The boys turned around slowly, hesitant to confront whatever it was that made such a monstrous sound. They gasped as one, terror holding them as firmly as the spruce trees rooted to the ground. Towering above them was a massive grizzly bear, standing ten feet high and weighing over a thousand pounds. A young cub stood nearby. The bear lowered its head and roared its anger at them, the noise as earsplitting as a thunderclap.

Tahteh stepped back as he groped for his quiver. It was enough to excite the grizzly bear as it shook the ground with its mighty step, its teeth bared and saliva dripping like foam from the sides of its mouth. In one sweeping motion, its mighty paw scooped Tahteh off the ground and sent him reeling twenty feet, spinning him like a bird shot from the air.

The sound of bones shattering and the dull thump of the boy's body hitting the ground awakened the full force of terror in Dakota. "Tahteh!" he cried, stumbling forward, then crawling toward him. Just then Peeshkoh wrestled Dakota to the ground, his voice hard and desperate in Dakota's ear.

"Stay on your hands and knees," he ordered. "Don't move. Press your body close to mine and hold still— no matter what. The bear is going to come after us. If you try to escape, we're both dead. I guarantee it!"

Peeshkoh's words struck Dakota like arrows flying in a buffalo hunt. He needed no further warning. He

hugged his body tight, letting his weight fall against his friend. The roar of the grizzly came crashing down on him, squeezing the life breath out of him. The steamy vapor of the bear breathed over his ears and down his neck, like hellfire.

Every instinct in Dakota screamed for him to get up and run, but the words of Peeshkoh were strong. He squeezed his eyes shut, pressing closer to his friend, feeling a slight nudge of encouragement. The knifelike claws of the grizzly ripped through his skin, gouging the softer flesh of his belly. The force of the animal threw Dakota ruthlessly from side to side as it tried to roll him over, the pain searing through him like daggers. A sharp jab from Peeshkoh begged Dakota not to panic. His friend's nearness and the realization that if he tried to run death was certain were the only considerations that kept him huddled to the ground.

The grizzly pulled away from the boys and lumbered over to the tree where Tahteh had fallen and began pawing and slapping at his limp body.

Dakota collapsed, overtaken by shock. From down a long tunnel he heard the words of Peeshkoh pleading, "It's not over yet. Be brave, *mitakola*. The bear will tire of us. We will pull through this."

Dakota's heart pounded against his chest as the ground shook with the walloping strides of the grizzly bear returning. For what seemed like a lifetime, the grizzly continued to maul them. Dakota tried to find the grayish-white clouds inside him, the faraway place where nothing could touch him. The only

thread that held him to the earth was Peeshkoh's words, "Be brave, *mitakola*."

Dakota had no idea how long they kept their faces to the ground, but he was aware of a stillness settling around him. He didn't dare move for fear the grizzly was watching and waiting from a distance. He wondered if Peeshkoh was sharing the same thoughts. He could hear soft breathing next to him, like the hollow whooshing the ocean makes at low tide. Taking a chance, Dakota felt for Peeshkoh. He caught the edge of his friend's breechcloth and held it firmly while he waited.

There was no longer any light, only darkness, making their situation all the more terrifying. All they could do was wait and listen. Through the silence the nighthawk, the forerunner of dusk, began its boisterous trilling. The richness of its song awakened Dakota's stronghold on life. No matter what, he would pull through this nightmare and encounter the next day with a strong heart.

Peeshkoh lifted his body in slow, deliberate stages. When he was on his knees he held himself perfectly still, listening for anything that moved. Not knowing the whereabouts of the grizzly was more nerve-racking than having it hovering over them.

Peeshkoh whispered from the side of his mouth, "Don't move. I am going to see if the bear has tired of us."

Dakota tried to protest, but his friend silenced him with a swift motion of his hand. Peeshkoh slipped away

so quietly Dakota had no idea what direction he had taken. The only sounds he heard were the hum of the mosquitoes and the sporadic chatter of the night birds.

Before he knew it, Peeshkoh was back at his side, lifting him up by his arms. Dakota moaned as he unfurled his body, every muscle and bone feeling as if they had been crunched underneath an avalanche.

"Can you walk?" asked Peeshkoh, holding Dakota under his arms to steady him.

"I think so," Dakota stammered. Streaks of fire burned across his back and undersides where the claws of the bear had dug into his flesh.

"Tahteh is dead," said Peeshkoh, his words so sudden they sounded unreal.

Dakota let this information settle inside him as the air grew thick and his stomach turned in nausea. He had no words for Peeshkoh.

"There is no sign of the bear or its cub," Peeshkoh said. "We must start a fire so we can find our way home."

When Dakota had as much kindling as he could carry, he shuffled along the dirt until he bumped into something. He made a startled cry like an animal, then felt a comforting hand on his shoulder. "Oh, it's you, Peeshkoh." He sighed as he emptied the leaves and branches into a pile, while his friend tried to make sparks by rubbing a straightening stone against another. Peeshkoh rubbed hard and fast until tiny sparks fell in a shower, then dissolved like fireflies. In anger, he struck with more force, his breathing slow and labored. Gradually, the sparks grew larger and

brighter. Peeshkoh moved closer to the kindling pile, working the straightening stones directly over them. A few of the branches ignited, sending up a small ribbon of smoke. Bending closer, the boys blew softly on the flame, bringing it to life.

Through the flickering light Peeshkoh and Dakota saw each other for the first time since the bear had attacked. Bile rose in Dakota's throat when he saw the long bloody welts running up and down Peeshkoh's left arm and side. Slipping behind his friend, he saw that his back was the same, with purple-blue blotches appearing as well.

Peeshkoh made a low whistling sound when he saw what the bear had inflicted upon Dakota. "*Mitakola*, my friend, you will carry the scars of this day for a long time."

Dakota sighed, thinking that life in Roundup wasn't so bad after all. "It is not easy living with the Sioux," he said.

"*Han*," agreed Peeshkoh. "You must be brave and strong at all times."

Peeshkoh and Dakota felt along the ground for their quivers and bows. "We must set fire to the ends of some arrows to make light," said Peeshkoh. "Then we will get Tahteh."

The boys' eyes met, each reflecting his own pain. Dakota drew back a few steps, his legs unsteady from the wretchedness that settled too deep in his gut to wrestle away. It was not easy for him to accept death. He had little instruction in religion, nor any binding faith from which to draw strength.

Dakota turned his face away from the tears gathering around his friend's eyes. It was a terrible thing to lose a friend like Tahteh, a true warrior, meant to die on the battlefield, not in the death grip of a grizzly bear.

Once they got the arrow tips burning, Peeshkoh stamped out the fire and handed his bow and quiver to Dakota, asking him to lead the way.

They reached Tahteh's body underneath the pine tree where he had fallen, like a frail bird, crumpled and broken, his hands covering his face. He had not died instantly as they had thought. When Peeshkoh pulled Tahteh's hands from his face they saw a hint of a smile, as if he found his last adventure with life amusing.

Peeshkoh lifted Tahteh's body in his strong arms, his face twisted from the pain. Dakota held the lit arrows high as he led the way through the darkness, searching for the narrow paths that would take them back to the clearing where the ponies were shackled. Their progress was slow and labored, with only the faintest light from the ends of the arrows to guide them through the tangle of branches and thick underbrush.

When they stepped from the dense forest into the obscure light of the half moon, the endless grasslands were a welcome sight. The ponies danced restlessly when they heard their footsteps, making the shackles around their feet jingle. When the boys drew near, the horses shook their shaggy manes and pawed the ground in response to the smell of bears on the boys.

They placed Tahteh's body over his gray and

white spotted mare, then unshackled the ponies. Peeshkoh drew some arrows from Tahteh's quiver and thrust them deep into the ground to mark the place where they had begun the elk hunt.

They rode back to camp with an uneasy silence settling between them. There was barely enough light from the moon to guide them to a clearing where they could see their village beyond the low rolling knolls, the lodges appearing like dark hillocks, lifeless without the fires burning inside them.

Dakota broke the silence. "I hope I will be able to slip inside the tepee without being noticed," he said. He figured there were only a few hours left before the sun would take them to a new day.

"Don't count on it," Peeshkoh warned. "Tatanka Iyotanka does not sleep until all his children are secure in their beds."

Mounted warriors of the *akicita*, those who keep order in the village, rode out to meet Peeshkoh and Dakota. When they drew close enough to hear, Peeshkoh told them it was only Wahpa Tanka Newne, the nephew of Tatanka Iyotanka, and Peeshkoh, nephew of Pizi. He explained what had happened, pointing to the body of Tahteh slung across his pony.

The *akicita* warriors shook their heads as their eyes wandered up and down the boys' tattered bodies, then far off to the Wolf Mountains. It was not a good thing to have the grizzly bear trampling through the hunting grounds.

The *akicitas* led Tahteh's pony to the Oglala village. They would watch over his body until his family was

informed of his death. There would be a ceremony and four days of mourning for their friend. From now on no one would speak Tahteh's name. It was the way of the Lakota in honoring their dead.

Dakota and Peeshkoh walked their ponies to the corral where they let them loose to graze in the blue-gray haze of predawn. Peeshkoh turned to Dakota. "I will follow you to your tepee," he offered. "If Tatanka Iyotanka is waiting for you, he will want an explanation."

They walked in silence, Dakota lingering over specific events of the day. It felt strange to return to camp without Tahteh alive, not hearing his easy laughter.

Circling around to the southern edge of the lodges, they found everything dark and quiet. Dakota breathed a sigh of relief. All he wanted was sleep, to put the pain and sorrow to rest for a while.

Dakota hesitated before entering the tepee. "We'll tell the others about the bear and elk tomorrow, when we're together. And about the rest—." His voice trailed off, leaving only a sigh to settle between them.

"Han," said Peeshkoh, rubbing his hands over his eyes.

As Dakota was about to slip inside the tepee, Peeshkoh leaned close and whispered, "Do not be so sure that no one stirs inside your lodge. I will wait to see if you get through this unnoticed."

Dakota nodded, too tired to say anything more. He entered through the flap door and tiptoed to the right, avoiding the side that Sitting Bull occupied. He

slumped wearily into the warm folds of the rug and closed his eyes.

Immediately, he drifted into the calm waves of half-sleep. Somewhere between the earth and the clouds, he thought he felt something pressing on his shoulder. He tried to ignore it, but the weight grew heavier and more persistent. Dakota sat up with a start. Sitting Bull was standing over him, motioning him to get up. Dakota pulled himself from the warmth of his bed like one carrying the weight of too much sorrow within him. He followed the chief, who carried his long pipe and some buffalo rugs tucked under his arm, through the door flap and into the night. Peeshkoh was still waiting outside, more sure of the ways of Tatanka Iyotanka than Dakota.

In the dusk of the half-moon and star-filled sky, Sitting Bull saw the ravaged bodies of Peeshkoh and Dakota and shook his head, saying, *"Hoksila witkotkoke."*

Peeshkoh let his words spill out like a fast-moving river, filling Tatanka Iyotanka's ears so fast that the chief held his hand up to quiet him for a moment. He laid a buffalo rug against the outside of the lodge and patted the ground on either side of him. As soon as the boys were settled next to Sitting Bull, the chief took his buffalo robe from behind his back and drew it across their shoulders. Dakota shivered under the blanket as he faced the moon and the stars, and the uncertainty of Sitting Bull's reaction.

Dakota listened as Peeshkoh began his story. He recognized a few Lakota words but not many. Every once in a while Sitting Bull would ask a question or

simply respond by saying, *"Aiii."* Halfway through the story Sitting Bull lit his pipe, then faced the tip to the earth, the sky, and the four directions.

Peeshkoh spoke softly, careful not to awaken the sleeping villagers. It was hard to stay awake underneath the warm buffalo rug and the sound of Peeshkoh's gentle voice. Even the smell of Sitting Bull's tobacco, with its rich cherry bark and sage leaves, had a lulling effect on his senses.

When Peeshkoh finished speaking, no one got up to leave. Perhaps it was the comfort of having Sitting Bull nearby, or maybe they were too tired to move. In any case, Peeshkoh and Dakota surrendered themselves to the night, both leaning wearily against the strong one in the middle.

CHAPTER 10

Three Stars and a Field of Rosebuds

Dakota awoke with a start, his heart racing and his teeth clenched in pain. He wiped the sweat and worry that trickled down his face and tried to piece together the remnants of a dream that drifted farther and farther from his grasp.

He thought it had been his mother he saw in the shadows, running barefoot under a darkening sky, tripping and falling over brambles and prickly shrubs that stood in her path. Each time she fell, she would pull herself up and take off again, the words "I have no one!" pursuing her like a hungry wolf. When she reached a tall black rock that stood alone near the riverbank, she threw herself against it, her arms hugging its smooth surface. Her gaze seemed to be drawn to the river that gurgled leisurely along a winding path. She stared for a long time into the glassy water, as if she were searching for something.

"Mother," Dakota whispered, unsure if it were really her he saw in the shadows. Slowly, her image

began to fade, dissolving into the folds of the water. Dakota called out again, his voice razor sharp, bringing him fully awake.

A lump rose painfully in his throat, bringing hot tears trickling down his cheeks. He wiped angrily at his face, embarrassed by his need to see his mother, to check on his grandfather, the horses, even the cows.

Through misty eyes Dakota watched as the light filtered through the open door of the tepee. It occurred to him that someone had carried him inside during the night. Probably Sitting Bull. He knew he must have slept a long time, as it was already *wicokan*, or noon. He wondered how much longer he would be staying with Sitting Bull, if Toskala were doing any better. There was something about her that reminded him of his mother, her boundless energy that could so easily give way to sadness. If they sent him back to Toskala, was he expected to keep an eye on her?

The events of yesterday crowded into Dakota's mind, forcing him out of the warm folds of his bed and into the daylight. He stood with only his breech-cloth hugging his lean waist, squinting against the bright light that temporarily blinded him. He rubbed his eyes several times, letting his gaze fall on the bloody welts that covered his body. For some reason they now seemed insignificant. The fact that he had escaped the grizzly bear at all was a miracle.

The air was soft and summery and so still he could hear the buzz of insects circling back and forth among the prairie flowers. Dakota stretched his arms in front of him and felt the tightness in his muscles

and the ache in his bones. He crossed in front of Toskala's tepee and noticed that the door flap was down and a thin line of smoke was rising through the opening where the lodge poles crossed. Usually at this time her door would be open and she would be busy preparing pemmican or getting the buffalo hides ready for the winter coats.

He drifted toward the river, his arms and legs moving as slowly as the sleepy village before him. When he passed the smoking fires of the Hunkpapa camp he inhaled the rich aroma of strong coffee and roasted elk, mixed with the bitter smell of boiling chokecherries and wild turnips. His stomach churned with hunger, but the emptiness he felt at that moment was too keen to satisfy with food.

Dakota stepped gingerly into the river, his body stiffening under the icy water that awakened the raw tenderness of his wounds. He jumped up and down as he lowered his body in stages. When the water rose to his neck, he reached to the bottom and brought up a handful of mud and patted it over the deep gouges that covered his body. It was cool and smooth against his raw skin, like a soothing hand calming the sharpness of his pain.

On either side of him children splashed in the water, shouting and laughing. A few women stood knee deep near the bank, the edges of their buckskin dresses skimming the surface as they dug for turnips. Seeing the village like this was strangely comforting. He understood better why Sitting Bull and Crazy Horse fought so hard to preserve this way of life.

"There could be no better way to live," he thought, admiring the easy way the women and children worked and played together and the respect they showed one another.

Once the mud had dried and cracked against his skin, Dakota dove into the water and swam farther and father until his lungs felt as if they would burst. He broke through the surface and gulped mouthfuls of air.

When Dakota stepped out of the water, a rush of contrary feelings washed over him and darkened his mood even more. Each footstep became heavier as he climbed the riverbank, every thought of yesterday more burdensome. It wasn't fair that Peeshkoh and he were alive and Tahteh would never ride his pony again in a buffalo hunt or earn the status of a warrior. But when he beheld the brilliant green and gold-flecked valleys rolling toward the brow of the sky in waves, his heart lifted like a bird and the center of his being swelled with the miracle of being alive.

His feet shuffled lazily across the warm ground until he was once again at the Hunkpapa camp. His mood lifted a little when he saw Peeshkoh leaning against Sitting Bull's lodge, his bowl and horn spoon in hand. "Have you eaten yet?" Peeshkoh called out.

"Not yet," he replied, stooping low to pass through the door of the tepee. Seeing his friend and smelling the elk somehow turned Dakota's appetite around. "I could eat until my stomach bursts," he said.

"You say that every day," said Peeshkoh, brushing aside Dakota's remark with a swish of his hand.

Dakota took his bowl and horn spoon from his

parfleche. "Well, today I mean it. I'm not used to eating only once a day."

"You can eat all you want today," said Peeshkoh. "The word is already out that we killed thirteen elk, and their bodies can be found at the edge of the Wolf Mountains, where a few arrows mark the passageway."

Dakota stiffened. He regarded his friend with a mixture of surprise and anger. They had agreed that they would wait until they could both tell the others about the elk.

Peeshkoh shook his head impatiently. "It was your *hunka*, Tatanka Iyotanka, who has been boasting to the entire village that three boys dropped thirteen elk, then stopped to wrestle a grizzly bear."

Dakota's face softened a little.

"Hoppo," said Peeshkoh, heading for the campfires. "I am also hungry."

Young girls were tending the boiling pots, turning the slabs of meat that dripped fat into the fire, making sounds that popped like the frozen trees in winter. Dakota slapped his stomach, making it sound like a hollow drum. Peeshkoh made a disgusting face. "You are always hungry," he complained. "Always ready to lick the fat from the boiling pots if one is ever offered to you."

"I wouldn't mind holding my tongue under the meat and letting the fat drip down my throat," returned Dakota, his mouth watering.

"I will ask the *wicincala* to be generous with us today," said Peeshkoh. He winked at Dakota, but the familiar spark of mischief wasn't there this time.

Peeshkoh held his bowl out to the nearest girl and bent close to her, whispering something in her ear. The girl flicked her braids back and watched Peeshkoh out of the corner of her eye. She then turned to Dakota and held her hand out to him. He gave her his bowl, wondering what Peeshkoh had said. The girl kept looking at Peeshkoh as she piled a generous amount of food onto Dakota's plate, even a few extra bones, thick with elk meat.

"You will eat well now," Peeshkoh said, his voice distant. He gazed down at his bowl and was silent.

Dakota also stared at the meat and thought of Tahteh. It was strange how after the events of yesterday everything seemed so normal, people talking and laughing, eating and sleeping, when they should have been doing something crazy like pounding their fists against a rock or screaming until their lungs burst.

The boys found a shaded spot underneath a willow tree, where they plopped down on the cool grass and started consuming their food right away. They both began with a juicy bone, biting into the warm, smoky meat, letting the fat drip down their chins. Between mouthfuls of meat and boiled turnips, Peeshkoh spoke leisurely. "There is talk at the Cheyenne camp that the bluecoats are marching along the Rosebud—at least a thousand of them—all under Three Stars."

Dakota froze at Peeshkoh's words. He had lost all track of time, not really wanting to think about it, somehow hoping his presence would change everything. He chewed slowly, pondering what his friend

had said. "What day is it anyway?" he asked, a note of concern in his voice.

Peeshkoh stopped eating and regarded Dakota as if he were trying to find some meaning in his question. After a long pause, he merely shrugged, then continued to eat again.

"The date, the month?" persisted Dakota. "Don't you know what day it is?"

Peeshkoh thought for a moment. "It's *Wipazuka Waste Wi*, June—the Moon of the Chokecherries."

"But what day is it?" asked Dakota, pressing his friend for an answer.

Peeshkoh narrowed his eyes at Dakota. "Why should I know? Only the white man lives his life by a timepiece."

Dakota thought for a moment. It was June—that much he knew. But who was Three Stars? He dug deeper into his memory. Then he remembered! He was General George Crook. The Battle of the Rosebud occurred on June 17, 1876, a decisive factor in the final outcome of the Battle of the Little Bighorn. Three Stars was marching toward the Rosebud with his thousand bluecoats! The idea shot through him like fire spurred by a strong wind, bringing a hot flush to his cheeks.

"What is the matter with you?" demanded Peeshkoh.

"Nothing's the matter!" Dakota shot back. He stared at his food, no longer hungry, the meat now tasteless. All he wanted at that moment was to mount Cahli and take off at fast speed, anywhere—to ride

forever with the wind hitting his face and the galloping drum of hooves beneath him.

Dakota surveyed the campsite. It was less noisy now that the girls had fed the hungry warriors and children, emptying all the cooking pots. He caught sight of Many Horses as she slipped past the door of her lodge and stood with her face tilted to the sun. The easy way she did this made Dakota's heart jump. He continued to watch her every movement, his stomach tightening into knots.

She wore a bright and warm smile as the sun caught the blue shimmers in her ebony hair. One of the wolf dogs that roamed freely around the camp leaped against her chest, almost knocking her over. She steadied herself, putting one foot forward and bending down so that she could wrap her arms around its neck and press her face into its furry chest.

Dakota felt something catch in his throat. He imagined it was him who Many Horses wrapped her arms around. He sighed, wondering why such pleasures were always out of his reach. He continued to watch the source of his happiness, when a young warrior dashed in front of her, sending swirls of dust and anxious cries into the shiftless afternoon. The horse came to a halt in front of Sitting Bull's lodge, pitching the camp into chaos.

Peeshkoh jumped to his feet. "Something is happening!" he cried, letting the scraps of food and bare bones fall to the ground, where the hungry dogs fell upon them in seconds.

A moment later, Sitting Bull emerged from his tepee, wearing only his breechcloth. His bare feet shuffled along the dirt, his slight limp from an old war injury singling him out from the others. Before he reached the mounted warrior, the young man began speaking hastily to Sitting Bull.

As the boys hurried to Sitting Bull's lodge, Peeshkoh told Dakota that the rider was Little Wolf, a Cheyenne scout. When they drew closer, Dakota heard Sitting Bull speak quietly, letting his words calm the excitement that the young rider had brought with him.

Warriors from each tribe began to gather around Sitting Bull, everyone talking above the next person, their strong arms sweeping across the air with great emphasis. Sitting Bull continued to speak in his quiet way, leading the men toward the great council lodge. Peeshkoh and Dakota followed in their wide shadows. Many more warriors joined the group, stirring up more dust and excitement as their numbers grew.

A large council lodge had been erected by combining several tepees. As Sitting Bull's followers gathered in bunches outside, a few of the older men propped the sides of the lodge up so that those who were not present within the council walls would still be able to hear the discussions from outside.

Dakota wrapped his arms around his chest, feeling small among so many great chiefs. Pizi had just joined Sitting Bull, his huge frame barely able to pass through the door. Touch the Clouds of the Minneconjous and

Two Moons and Old Bear of the Cheyenne exchanged words before entering. After Black Moon and Crow King of the Hunkpapas had disappeared inside, Crazy Horse and Little Big Man made their way past the throng, bringing a hush to the younger boys, who stared wide-eyed at the Oglalas, both war leaders, no more than thirty-five winters and already able to boast of many coups.

The talking went on for many hours, growing louder and more animated as the sun dropped steadily toward the mountain peaks. A blaze of scarlet lit the sky, creating a bloody curtain that fell behind the ebony mountains. Dakota could not remember ever seeing the sky so bright and sharp before. He started to draw Peeshkoh's attention to it when an excited cry spread among those seated outside the lodge tent.

Peeshkoh whooped and cheered, the hot blood of revenge reflected in his eyes. "We will fight Three Stars and his bluecoats," he cried, his fists clenched so tightly his knuckles turned white.

He is ready, thought Dakota, ready to kill the soldiers so he can quiet his angry heart. Peeshkoh grabbed Dakota's arm. "We must get our weapons and our ponies, and then I will tell you what the chiefs said."

When they arrived at Dakota's lodge, a buzz of excitement swirled among the women as they filled the parfleches in the event the village was attacked. The twin boys of Sitting Bull were crying loudly, but no one seemed to care at that moment. Dakota pulled his parfleche from under his buffalo rug and stuffed his T-

shirt, sweatshirt, and leggings inside. He snatched his bow and quiver and buffalo rug and was outside in the fading sunlight in a matter of minutes.

Dakota walked briskly alongside Peeshkoh, his feet keeping rhythm with the excitement that beat within him. He could hear the fervor passing through the camps, the warriors stirring up fires in even those who had spoken against attacking the bluecoats.

Dakota wondered where all of this would take him? What part could he possibly play? He wasn't sure he could take sides against the Bluecoats or the Sioux. He had been doing that long enough with his own parents. His father was as proud of his Irish heritage as Savannah was of being Lakota. It seemed to Dakota that their cultural differences had become more pronounced over the years, and he found himself wavering somewhere in the middle, unwilling to side with either parent and unable to claim either heritage as his own.

As they passed Toskala's lodge, Dakota grabbed Peeshkoh's arm and stopped him. "Come with me to see how Toskala is doing."

"Toskala? Why do you need to see her?"

Dakota was surprised at the harshness in Peeshkoh's tone. "She's been very sick," he explained. "A few days ago I had to get Sitting Bull. She couldn't even hold a cup in her hands."

Peeshkoh was watching the other warriors as they readied themselves for battle, some painting their horses, others making sure their weapons were

in order. He turned impatiently to Dakota. "Toskala has a son to look after her. She does not need you to get in her way."

"Where?" demanded Dakota. "I haven't seen anyone else in her tepee. Does he know how sick she is?"

Peeshkoh let out a long sigh. "Tahca Luzahan is busy looking for a wife among the Brules."

"But isn't he Hunkpapa?" Dakota asked.

"*Han*," said Peeshkoh, "He is Hunkpapa, but there are too many chiefs among our people. His chances are better with the Brules, if he can find a woman with good standing, and one who will have him as husband."

Dakota wanted to see for himself if Toskala were better, then he would be on his way. He didn't think her son would be checking on her anytime soon. He turned toward her lodge and called over his shoulder, "I won't be long."

Peeshkoh followed close behind Dakota. "I do not understand why Toskala is any concern of yours," he snarled.

Dakota ignored Peeshkoh and called out in a loud voice, "*Hau!* It's me, Dakota. Can I come in?"

Peeshkoh pushed his way past Dakota. "Let me do the talking. You will only confuse and anger her if you speak in the white man's tongue."

Toskala clasped Peeshkoh's hands as they talked, her eyes seeming to plead for something she desperately wanted. Dakota thought she looked a little better, but she was still wrapped in her buffalo rugs, her voice as rough and dry as her wrinkled face.

Despite Peeshkoh's earlier impatience, he dis-

played a gentleness in his manner as he stroked Toskala's hand, and his soothing words carried a note of reassurance.

As they were leaving, Toskala's voice trailed after them. When Dakota turned around, she lifted a frail hand and smiled at him. There was a sadness in her eyes that Dakota noticed right away. He waved back, thinking how lonely it must be for her with no husband and a son who spent most of his time away from her.

When they were outside, Peeshkoh explained that Toskala wanted them to find her son. His eyes were thin slits when he frowned at Dakota. "How can we do that when we must fight the *wasicu*?"

"Maybe we can catch up with him at the Brules' camp?" Dakota offered.

"And then what? Do you think he is going to run home to his mother when there is a battle to be fought?"

Dakota shrugged, too tired to respond. His head was aching with the uncomfortable position in which he found himself. What was he doing following Peeshkoh to the Rosebud, anyway? What would he do if a *wasicu* tried to kill him? He shook the thought away and ran to keep up with his friend.

They found Pizi inside his lodge by the fire, eating with an appetite that could easily satisfy five men. His young daughter sat across from him, talking animatedly about something. Pizi nodded between mouthfuls, never once taking his eyes off her.

When Peeshkoh finished stuffing all he could into his parfleche, he turned to Pizi and exchanged a

few hurried words with him, then left with Dakota.

While the boys readied their ponies, Peeshkoh told Dakota how Tatanka Iyotanka had tried to convince the warriors not to fight the soldiers but to wait and see if the soldiers attacked them. Many of the older warriors agreed with Sitting Bull, saying that only bad things would come to them if they were the first to attack. But many of the Cheyenne could not sit still with such cautious words. For ten years they carried the betrayal heavy on their shoulders, never forgetting how the *wasicus* had attacked and burned their village at Sand Creek while the people slept. Hundreds of Black Kettle's people, most of them women and children, were slaughtered as they tried to escape. The Cheyenne had always been a peaceful tribe before that, moving here and there as the white man dictated.

"*Aiii*," wailed Peeshkoh, his anger boiling from the retelling of such wrongs. "The young warriors said, 'No!' to Tatanka Iyotanka. They would seek out Three Stars themselves and bloody the *wasicus'* camp with the soldier's blood this time."

"Isn't Pizi going to fight?" Dakota asked, wondering why Peeshkoh was in such a hurry and Pizi wasn't.

"In time he will come with his followers," Peeshkoh explained. His expression grew serious as he regarded Dakota, like one measuring another's worth. "It is the younger warriors who are eager to get started. It is you and I who must prove ourselves, not Pizi."

Dakota and Peeshkoh rode at a full gallop to the Oglala camp. They found Crazy Horse and his warriors getting ready for the long ride ahead. Crazy

Horse stood beside his wife, Black Shawl, who was helping him paint lightning streaks and hailstones on his spotted gray horse.

A thin gray light helped guide those who followed the young Oglala leader, who rode at the front of the line, maintaining a fast trot throughout the long night.

When daybreak finally encircled the weary travelers, they came upon the big bend that empties into the Rosebud. Shallow hills rolled in waves of emerald green, dotted everywhere with clusters of delicate rosebuds. It was before this beautiful valley that the Sioux and Cheyenne readied themselves for battle.

As was the habit with Crazy Horse, he loosened his hair and tied a calfskin cape over his shoulders. He bent to the ground and scooped up a handful of dust and poured it over his horse for protection during battle.

The other warriors began their careful preparations as well. Peeshkoh insisted on painting Dakota's face like a Lakota warrior. Dakota let him smear the black paint all over his face and run two white lines down either cheek. Dakota did the same for Peeshkoh. When he was finished, he couldn't help but laugh. For him, none of it seemed real. It was as if they were playing some sort of game. Peeshkoh crushed his laughter with harsh words that left him speechless. An uncomfortable silence settled between them, becoming more awkward when neither chose to break it.

Crazy Horse sent a few scouts ahead to see if they could locate Three Stars and his bluecoats. They hadn't been gone long before they ran into some

Crow scouts, who were working for Three Stars. A piercing war cry rang across the still valley. Crazy Horse turned to his men and cried, *"Hoke hey!"* He shot forward on his horse, a man full of purpose. As the warriors swooped into the valley, they saw the Crows fleeing to the camp of Three Stars, shouting their warnings: "Sioux coming! Sioux coming!"

Crazy Horse raised his lance high above his head and called over his shoulder, *"Yi-hoo!"* The warriors followed like a stampeding herd of buffalo, their horses pounding the earth and their war cries bellowing across the bluffs.

Peeshkoh and Dakota fell to the rear. They did not speak to one another. Dakota rode as if he were in a dream, bursting with joy at being part of such a magnificent band—the Plains Indians—surely the finest warriors ever to live. He felt a part of them at that moment. They were in his blood as sure as his mother's blood was in him. The wind hit his face in great gusts. As he inhaled its power, he became a part of it as well. "I will not die," he told himself, wearing the invincible shield of youth, his spirit flying as fast as his galloping pony.

Crazy Horse ordered his warriors to hold back and stay together as the first line of bluecoats trotted forward, more rows forming quickly behind the first. General Crook moved to the center of the field, where he ordered his men to attack. During the first charge, one of the bluecoats' horses broke loose and ran straight for the swarm of warriors. The Indians shot at the soldier as his horse drew within several

yards of them. Miraculously, the soldier was able to turn his horse around, but not quite soon enough. As he galloped back to his troops, flying bullets shot off both his hands. Dakota watched in a stupor as the man rode toward his fellow soldiers with his hands dangling from his wrists.

Crazy Horse and his warriors backed their horses toward the rocks, acting as if they were hesitant to attack. As the troops advanced, the soldiers scattered in small groups. As soon as this happened, Crazy Horse cried, *"Hokahe!"* and together he and his followers charged at the soldiers, half of his warriors attacking the right flank and the other half the left.

The battle was in full force—a thousand warriors charging against a thousand bluecoats, the horses baying frantically as the buzz of bullets and arrows whistled around them. A layer of dust rose thick as morning fog, helping to disguise somewhat the barbaric sight of the warriors as they swung their tomahawks recklessly through the air, while the bluecoats reloaded their rifles as fast as they could fire them.

Dakota found himself in the middle of a hundred horses, the Indians yelping and whirling their mounts in tighter circles, dust and bullets and arrows flying everywhere, bodies crumpling and hitting the ground like so many pinecones blown from a tree. Only an arm's length away from Dakota, a soldier flew off his horse and fell with a thud to the ground, squirming in his own blood as the horses stampeded over him. Frantically, Dakota tried to pull Cahli away from the fighting, but horses were pushing in all around him,

the air so stifling he could barely breathe. He snatched an arrow from his quiver and set it on his bow, at the same time searching for the enemy. Only a few yards away he spotted a bluecoat, his brow set in hard lines as he fired bullet after bullet at his enemy.

Dakota pulled his bowstring back and took aim, but every inch of his body froze at that moment, making it impossible for him to cast his arrow.

From the distance a clearing opened, allowing Dakota to see beyond all the dust and turmoil. He thought he saw a familiar figure racing toward the inferno, many more following him. He squinted against the sun, hoping he was right. As the rider drew closer, Dakota sighed. It was Sitting Bull all right. He was like a cloud of smoke in the distance—he didn't look like much until he drew up close, stared him in the eyes— then he knew the power of the man, knew the hold he had on his people.

Sitting Bull must have sensed Dakota's distress, for he wasted no time thrusting his way past the horses and grabbing his reins. He led him far beyond the bluffs to an elevated ridge where the Sioux horses were being watched by a boy no more than thirteen. Sitting Bull left Dakota without so much as a nod and rode off to where Crazy Horse had been joined by Pizi and more Hunkpapas.

Dakota fussed over his quiver, trying to hide his shame and confusion. How quickly his moment of glory had been crushed by the sight of battle and the bold hand of Sitting Bull, leading him away like a mere child to keep guard of the horses. He was sure

that Peeshkoh was out there somewhere, galloping courageously among the bluecoats, distinguishing himself as a brave warrior.

Dakota peered over the horses and watched as three separate battles occurred at once. The circle that Dakota had been caught in earlier was now in the thick of it. There were Cheyenne and Sioux coming from every direction, climbing the ridge and closing in on the bluecoats faster than coyotes on a fallen deer.

At the edge of the bluff, seated on a majestic black stallion, Dakota was sure he saw the proud figure of Captain Guy Henry, his deep voice booming out encouragement to his men as he fired his rifle. At one point the captain stopped and shielded his eyes with his hand, trying to see beyond the bluffs where more troops were trying to make their way toward him. Reinforcements were badly needed. A loud blast shot through the air. Captain Henry's body jerked forward, a bullet passing completely through his left cheek and out his right. It seemed as if the captain fell in slow motion, first slumping forward on his horse, then rolling off and spilling onto the ground in a heap.

Crazy Horse and his warriors saw this as well. They sprinted forward, eager to surround the body, eager to count first coup on an officer's scalp. As fast as the Sioux rode toward the fallen victim, the Crows and the Shoshones who fought for the bluecoats did the same, all arriving together. They dismounted at once, as was the way with Indians fighting at close range. They fell into the kind of battle they knew best, a hand-to-hand struggle, all for the captain's body.

Dakota remounted Cahli so he could get a better view. His skin prickled at the sight of so many warriors clashing and swinging their lances and long-edged knives at one another, the silver tips of their weapons reflecting streaks of light from the blazing sun. Their painted bodies dodged and swirled as their beautiful headdresses flapped behind them like the wings of a hundred exotic birds.

From outside the raging circle, more Sioux and Cheyenne came, their bodies hugging the sides of their horses as they shot their rifles from underneath the necks of their mounts, leaving little of themselves exposed to oncoming bullets.

By late morning most of the Hunkpapas had arrived, bringing with them more rifles and fresh horses. Many of the warriors turned their weary horses over to Dakota and the other boy and returned to the field with new mounts. Crazy Horse came too, trading his spotted horse for his bay. Dakota watched in awe as the Oglala leader rode far to the left, naked of any paint and adornments, ready to join the Cheyenne, who were now in the thick of fighting near the river's edge.

When the dust had settled somewhat, Dakota saw a handful of soldiers moving in on a wounded Cheyenne whose horse had gotten away from him. From across the bluff, a horse came charging past the soldiers, stopping only long enough for the Cheyenne to mount behind the rider. Dakota leaned forward and gaped in stunned silence. The rider was a woman! It was Buffalo Calf Road charging bravely past the flying

bullets, risking her own life to save her brother, Comes-in-Sight.

Brother and sister circled and dodged the fighting soldiers, their bodies pressed closely together, hugging the side of the horse. A loud chanting broke out among the Cheyenne when Buffalo Calf Road made it to their clearing. It would become the most talked about exploit of their people—The Battle Where the Sister Saved Her Brother.

From Dakota's position that day, he saw many brave deeds performed. Whenever possible, the Sioux risked their lives to rescue the wounded or retrieve dead comrades who lay beyond the enemy line. Seeing such fearlessness made Dakota itch to be part of it, but he was unable to take sides. Counting coup was one thing, killing was another.

Maybe his *hunka* sensed his need, or maybe it was by chance that Sitting Bull appeared at his side at that moment, signaling him to follow. Dakota rode east with Sitting Bull's band, following a path close to the Rosebud River. To their left, the bluecoats continued to defend themselves in the heaviest fighting, their numbers dropping by the hour. On the south side, another command of soldiers fought the Sioux, holding their own as best they could.

As they drew closer to the bluecoats' campsite, Dakota was surprised at how deserted it was. Apparently all of Crook's men were engaged in the heavy fighting. Sitting Bull and Dakota drew up to the riverbank, where a Shoshone boy, no more than ten winters, was watching the cavalry horses. One of the

Hunkpapa warriors dismounted and crept up behind him. He pointed his long-range rifle at the boy's back and fired. The small frame fell forward, hitting the ground as softly as a leaf blown from a tree.

Dakota could no more help the cry that escaped his lips than he could the outrage that welled up inside of him. He grabbed a handful of Cahli's mane to steady himself, trying hard not to think about a young boy whose life could be snuffed out so easily. "If you are old enough to go to battle, you are old enough to die." Those had been Peeshkoh's words to him when they were readying themselves for battle. "Only words," he thought. They did nothing to right the horror of what he had just witnessed.

The warrior lifted a handful of the boy's hair from the back of his head and cut the scalp as easily as if he were skinning a rabbit. Holding the bloody scalp above his head, he trilled a cry of victory. Dakota turned away and stared into the slow-moving river, everything numb inside him.

Sitting Bull was already untying some of the horses, as were many of his followers. Dakota dug his heels roughly into Cahli's flanks and rode to the front of the herd. He leaned back on his pony and surveyed the horses with a keen eye. He discovered two majestic stallions standing side by side, as white as powdery snow.

As he slipped the reins from over their heads, Dakota heard the heavy pounding of hooves coming fast and with determination. *"Akicitas! Hoppo!"* cried Sitting Bull, driving four more horses to the group his

warriors had gathered. The Hunkpapas made a wild dash, pushing the herd in front of them, swinging in a northwesterly direction. Dakota glanced nervously over his shoulder. The bluecoats were closing in fast, the nostrils of their horses flaring and snorting as their riders raced them at full gallop.

On impulse, Dakota veered to the left, separating himself from Sitting Bull's band. The bluecoats continued in hot pursuit after the Hunkpapas, determined to rescue their stolen horses. One of Sitting Bull's men fell from a bullet, his body tumbling backward off his horse. Sitting Bull continued to circle to the right, keeping a safe distance from the fighting.

Dakota drove the stallions far beyond the eastern bluffs, moving them northeast, sweeping as far away from the battlefield as he could. To his left, two thousand men continued to fight for their lives. For the Sioux and Cheyenne though, it was more than that—they fought for their very existence as a people, as a culture that had reigned supreme for many years on the Great Plains.

Dakota flew so fast across the prairie that any worry of being shot blew away with the wind. He knew he would make it, that he would score at least one victory today. He sped past trees and ravines, dodging rocks and breaks in the ground, pumping his horses as fast as they could be driven. When he reached the place where Sitting Bull had first left him, he came to a skidding halt, swirling the dust around Sitting Bull and his Hunkpapas, who had also just arrived. They had lost one warrior, but their victory

was evident as a dozen of the bluecoats' horses joined the circle of Sioux horses.

Sitting Bull said something that made the others turn their gaze on Dakota and laugh. He blushed as pink as the rosebuds that filled the valley. Despite his discomfort, he stared at the white chargers that were now his, marveling at how he had managed to bring them halfway around the battlefield without mishap. Perhaps, like Crazy Horse and Little Big Man, he too had good medicine that day, a guiding spirit watching over him.

Dakota searched the valley until he caught sight of Crazy Horse pushing his warriors hard against the bluecoats, forcing them southeastward along a creek. On the other side, Pizi led his men northward along the canyon, making the circle complete around General Crook's men. Many soldiers fell from their horses, spilling their blood all over the valley.

Dakota squinted against the blur of dust and gunpowder, until he saw a large, bearded man at the center of the field, mounted on a white stallion. General Crook was slumped in his saddle, his battered hat pressed low over his forehead, his braided beard flat against his face. He seemed to be viewing the carnage in front of him as one who sees his dreams crumbling into so many particles of dust, impossible to put together again. Suddenly, the general sat up and began shouting orders right and left, then galloped off toward the higher bluffs.

The bluecoats began circling behind Crazy Horse and attacking with a vengeance. Crazy Horse

ordered his warriors to retreat to the canyon, ending the Rosebud Battle midafternoon.

Sitting Bull and his Hunkpapas led their horses eastward, where they joined Crazy Horse. Together, the warriors began the long trek back to the village. Dakota fell to the rear of the procession, letting plenty of space fall between him and the last warrior. He waited until the last horse had disappeared behind a bend, then slipped off Cahli, grabbing his parfleche at the same time.

Below him the river bubbled and surged over mighty rocks that jetted out of the water. Along the riverbank, the June roses had opened in full bloom, swaying gently in the breeze that blew from the north. It was a crazy notion, but Dakota wanted to pick flowers for Many Horses. He didn't have the words to tell her how he felt, so he would let the flowers do the talking for him.

He selected the prettiest pink roses he could find and dropped each one gingerly inside his parfleche. Satisfied with what he had collected, Dakota slipped into his T-shirt and tied his sweatshirt around his waist. Once he was remounted, he had no trouble getting Cahli into a gallop. The pony was as eager as Dakota to get back to the village, to get as far away from the battlefield and the deadly hush that had settled so eerily across the Rosebud Valley.

CHAPTER 11

Dancing under a Full Moon

From all around the village, the loud keening rose and fell from those who had lost their loved ones at the Rosebud. Dakota stumbled past the line of tepees, searching for Peeshkoh and a way to rid himself of his own wretchedness. He got no farther than the edge of the Hunkpapa village when he came upon a young woman hacking viciously at her hair. When it was no more than a jagged line above her shoulders, she turned the knife into the tender flesh of her inner arm and let her shrill cries express the hurt inside.

Dakota closed his eyes as an image of his mother stole inside his mind. It had been almost two years since he had found her slumped against the foot of her bed, a knife and a pool of blood in her lap. He had remained surprisingly calm, wrapping her wrists in pillow cases, calling 911, then holding her hand as they wheeled her to an ambulance outside.

That night something snapped inside of him, leaving him paralyzed. He no longer knew how to act in

front of her. He couldn't shake the image of the knife and the blood, or the siren wailing down the street. Most of all, he couldn't rid himself of the fact that she had chosen to leave him.

A steel hand came crashing down on Dakota's back. He wheeled around, coming face to face with Peeshkoh, who was grinning from ear to ear.

"Mitakola!" Peeshkoh cried. "You look like you saw a grizzly bear." He punched Dakota in the stomach and laughed.

Dakota returned a feeble laugh as he wiped the sweat from his brow. "You are too ugly to be a grizzly bear," he said. "I thought you were a badger creeping up on me."

"A *hoka?*" Peeshkoh scrunched up his face. "That ugly, huh?"

Dakota's laugh was more casual this time. "Yeah, that ugly. You will have a hard time finding a girl to dance with you tonight."

Peeshkoh grinned in a boyish way. They both knew that he would have more girls to dance with than any other boy.

"I have seen Tahca Luzahan," Peeshkoh announced triumphantly. "He was fighting at the Rosebud, showing the Brules what a brave and daring warrior he is. I told him about Toskala when we were exchanging our ponies for fresh ones." Peeshkoh stopped talking and regarded Dakota with malicious delight. "Do you know what he said?"

Dakota sighed in exasperation. "Of course I don't! Why don't you just tell me."

"He said he heard there was a new boy at our village, one who was taking good care of his mother." Peeshkoh paused to see if his words had any effect on Dakota.

Dakota raised an eyebrow in a questioning slant. "What else? Has he returned? Has he seen her?"

"Humph," Peeshkoh snorted. "He has seen her this morning, but it is Toskala who now cares for him."

"What do you mean?" Dakota asked. He thought he detected a wry smile cross Peeshkoh's face.

"Tahca Luzahan had his ear blown off by a bullet. There are some who say he had it coming for not listening to their advice."

"His ear?" Dakota asked, feeling the blood drain from his face. His great great grandfather, Swift Deer, had lost his left ear in battle. He ran his hands up and down his arms. "What does Tahca Luzahan mean in English?"

Peeshkoh's eyes darkened with suspicion. "Why do you want to know?"

Dakota bent down to pet one of the village dogs. "I was only wondering if his mother gave him a name worthy of a warrior, or one better suited to his character."

"His name is Swift Deer," Peeshkoh said, humor twinkling in his eyes. "An appropriate name for one who takes off so quickly, then vanishes."

"Swift Deer!" Dakota tried to regain his composure. "I bet it won't be long before he runs off again to the Brules," he stated casually.

Peeshkoh slapped Dakota on the back. "That is what I was about to tell you, *mitakola*. It will not be long before Tahca Luzahan slips away, leaving you all alone to care for Toskala once again."

He shook his head at Peeshkoh, who was now heading back to his lodge, his shoulders shaking with laughter. "She takes care of me, too!" Dakota shouted after his friend.

When his chores were finished, Dakota stole away to the pony corral, carrying his parfleche with him. He couldn't help thinking about Swift Deer, his great great grandfather. He had been led to believe that he was a very great man, brave and generous among his people. He was beginning to wonder if everyone in his family, including his ancestors, were destined to run off at the first sign of trouble. Maybe all their problems began with Swift Deer. He thought about what Savannah had said about their past, how they were all connected somehow with their ancestors. He would have a long, hard look at Tahca Luzahan, he decided, and he would see for himself what kind of a man he truly was.

At the pony corral, Dakota rounded up the two white stallions and led them to the river, aware of the many eyes that followed him. "When I am finished with you," he told the horses, "you will have the entire village admiring you."

He found a spot near the river where the bank

flattened into a square patch of level ground. He emptied his parfleche, arranging the items he had borrowed from Toskala in a neat row: a piece of rawhide, a brush made from the tail of a porcupine, and a bowl made from a turtle shell. In the shell he poured some oil that had been made by boiling wild grass and love vine together to make soap.

Dakota led the first horse to the deepest level in the river, where he splashed water all over it, wetting even the mane and tail. He dipped his hands into the slippery oil and rubbed it across every inch of the horse. The soap slipped through his fingers like sheets of satin as he rubbed hard against the thick coat. His mind drifted to the upcoming dance, only hours away. If he were lucky, he would dance at least one dance with Many Horses. The thought made his knees quake. He laughed out loud, aroused by the possibility of what the night might hold for him.

When the first horse was soaped down and thoroughly rinsed, Dakota tied it to a nearby cottonwood tree and began the same process with the other horse. It was not long before he had their coats glistening like melting snow. While he worked the rawhide strip in circular motions up and down the horses, the sun beat down in waves on them so their coats were soon warm and silky to the touch.

Above Dakota an eagle flew in wide circles. He stopped what he was doing to watch it. There was something familiar in the way it swooped down from the sky, then circled around and around. He concen-

trated with all his might, trying to find some hidden message behind the bird's presence, for the secret behind the graceful way the wings spread so far and wide. As the eagle soared upward, Dakota saw something fall from the sky, spiraling gently downward, around and around, until it landed at his feet.

He ran his fingers over its smooth edges. It was a perfectly shaped eagle feather, mostly white with a splash of black at the tip. He looked skyward and followed the eagle as it dipped low once again, then soared upward, so far into the sky it was eventually lost to his view.

A gift, wondered Dakota, for the offering he was about to make? He fell back against the cool grass and stared at the sky. An image kept pressing into his thoughts, a familiar place where a large black rock stood by itself along the riverbank, beckoning him. He tried to shake the image from his mind, but it would not let go, it kept pushing inside of him, unshakable.

Spurred by a more pleasant thought, Dakota leaped to his feet and plunged into the river. The chill water cut through him, stirring him to such a pitch he was sure he would burst.

Dakota retrieved a handful of soap from the turtle shell and rubbed the silky oil all over his body and hair, working the oil into a rich, foamy lather. Charged with energy, he swam the width of the river and back again.

Returning to his horses, Dakota ran the porcupine brush over each one, rubbing them from their

heads to their hooves. The manes and tails he brushed more carefully, using long, even strokes until the hair glistened in silvery-white strands.

Now that he was finished, Dakota stepped back to admire his work. "Man-o-man-o-man!" He had snagged the finest looking horses he had ever seen! How was it possible? He smiled at the thought that they might have belonged to the general himself. He pressed his face into the downy neck of one of the stallions and breathed the warm sweet smell of oil and animal flesh. Many Horses will nestle her face in this same spot he told himself, smiling.

Dakota emptied the roses and sinew strips from his parfleche. He twisted and braided six long pieces together, forming a thin rope that ran three feet long. With great care he slipped each stem into the braided sinew, his head bent close to his work, heedful not to damage a single rose. When he was finished he held the wreath in front of him, feeling good about his work. The sun shone through each delicate pink and white petal. "The slightest wind can scatter them as easily as the rosebuds that blew across yesterday's battlefield," he thought.

He placed the wreath gently over the neck of one of the stallions and stepped back to see what effect it had. The horse looked as if it had stepped out of the pages of a fairy tale, the kind of horse a princess would ride.

With each step Dakota took toward Sitting Bull's lodge, his chest swelled with pride. He was sure he

would find the chief and his daughter inside, getting ready for the dance. As he passed the first line of tepees, people stopped and stared at the beautiful horses that paraded behind him. He glanced over his shoulder and felt his heart flutter. The stallions were prancing elegantly, lifting each leg high, as if they were marching in an exhibition, as if they had been bred for such an occasion.

As he neared Sitting Bull's lodge, a line of women and children gathered behind the horses, curious to see what Dakota was doing. He quickened his pace, anxious to put this moment behind him. He called out in a loud voice, using their Lakota names, "Tatanka Iyotanka! Sunkawakan Ota!"

Tatanka Iyotanka emerged first at the doorway, a stooped figure who quickly rose to his full height, powerful and imposing. Behind him, Many Horses appeared, peeking shyly behind her father. Dakota handed one of the horses to the Hunkpapa chief. The one wearing the beautiful wreath of roses he slipped to Many Horses, wrapping her fingers gently around the lead rope. The villagers trilled loudly, their faces showing surprise and wonder at such a show of generosity.

Dakota stole a furtive look at both father and daughter, just long enough to see the way Sitting Bull regarded him with a mixture of admiration and surprise. He passed through the door of the lodge, feeling giddy. He had also glimpsed the smile on the face of Many Horses just before she buried her face into the neck of the stallion, the flowers falling across her

hair, as he had imagined they would. He closed his eyes and kissed the black tip of his eagle feather. It was time to get ready for the dance.

Peeshkoh looked sideways at Dakota as they walked toward the noise and the yellow glow of the great campfire. "You look different today," he said. Dakota's hair was brushed back from his face with only a few strands falling across his forehead. He wore a new cotton shirt that Four Robes had made from the soft blue and white checkered material Sitting Bull had obtained from one of the traders. Over his neck hung several strands of beads and shells that Dakota had made himself. "Are you trying to impress someone?" Peeshkoh teased.

"I don't need to impress anyone," countered Dakota. "All the girls will be flocking after me. But I have only one girl on my mind." A warm smile lit his face.

"Yes," said Peeshkoh, patting him on the back. "We all know who that girl is—the one with the many horses. A name well chosen, wouldn't you say?"

"Who do you like?" Dakota asked, stirring the conversation away from himself. He had never seen Peeshkoh single out any one girl.

"Oh, I'm interested in all of them," Peeshkoh replied, running a hand over the otter fur that covered his waist-long braids. "Unlike you, *mitakola*, I will not deprive a single girl from the pleasure of dancing with

me." He rubbed his hands together, a smug grin on his face.

Dakota stopped for a moment to observe the hundreds of villagers already gathered outside the circle the boys had made in anticipation of the girls' arrival. The fire crackled and leaped almost as high as the lodge poles, sending with it the bitter smell of pine and the sweet aroma of sarsaparilla.

Dakota had to run to catch up with his friend, who strode eagerly toward the crowd. He would stay close to Peeshkoh for awhile, until a little of his friend's boldness rubbed off on him.

They watched in silence as the young girls made their way toward the circle, their faces bright with the anticipation of choosing their partners. They wore their finest dresses of soft yellow buckskin, heavily beaded, with fringes hanging from the sleeves and bottoms. Most of the girls wore their hair in long braids that hung over their chests.

Dakota searched for the one he could no longer free from his mind. The drums began to beat. The girls circled around the boys, their eyes searching mischievously for the ones they would claim as their dance partners. Right away a young girl grabbed Peeshkoh's hand and led him to the center. Dakota smiled to himself. He recognized her as the one who had been so generous with the meat the day before, the one who had smiled so secretively at Peeshkoh.

Dakota waited, searching the many faces of the girls, growing more anxious as boy after boy joined the circle, each striding forward, flaunting his self-

importance to those who were left behind. Each beat of the drum seemed to draw him farther away from his happiness. He wished more than ever that he had stayed behind and done as Crazy Horse had: gone off to hunt in the quiet of sundown.

The dancers whirled past him, their circle growing wider as they pushed those on the outside farther and farther back. As Dakota stepped backward, he felt the swish of one of the girl's dresses brush his arm. He swallowed his disappointment and looked far out to the prairie where the land seemed to join the stars and the sky. He wished he could blend into the land like that—disappear without anyone noticing.

A touch, soft and tentative, made him jump. He turned to see the eyes of Many Horses smiling at him. She took his hand and led him to the circle. He felt as light as air, if that was possible. He knew his face probably gave him away. Surely she would know by looking at him that she was the only girl who could bring such happiness to him.

Every beat of the drum, every sound in the night, throbbed within him, making him feel a part of the earth, the sky, and the air he breathed. It was as if all the world had come together for this moment. He noticed that the other boys danced with their arms around the necks of the girls, their bodies almost touching. He wanted to do the same, but his shyness held him back. At that moment he saw Sitting Bull coming toward them. Dakota's legs stiffened. Would Sitting Bull take his daughter away? Or would he haul Dakota away?

Sitting Bull took Dakota's arms and put them around his daughter, using the first English words he had ever heard him speak: "More fun this way." Dakota, though dumbfounded, smiled gratefully at Sitting Bull, who slipped away quietly, leaving them alone to find their own way.

Dakota couldn't help the grin that spread foolishly across his face as he stepped a little closer to Many Horses, his legs brushing against the fringes on her dress. He gazed at the full moon, as bright as the joy inside him. I won't forget this, he told himself, drawing every detail of the night into his soul, the quickening drumbeat, the intoxicating smells, the glow on Many Horses's face. Following the feet of the other dancers, he let the fervor catch him, let it carry him to the other side of the world and back again.

CHAPTER 12

The Battle of the Little Bighorn

On the twenty-fourth day of the Moon of the Chokecherries, the Cheyenne scouts followed a great herd of elk toward the Little Bighorn River. The great encampment moved north along the meandering river, stirring up great clouds of dust. The sun blazed hot, drawing many eyes to the cold river that gushed and gurgled. They crossed Ash Creek and rode two miles toward a flat stretch of land. Here, the Hunkpapas stopped, setting up their great circle at the southern end. The Cheyenne continued another four miles to the north where they stopped and arranged their camp. The other five bands settled as usual between the two great circles.

Dakota's skin prickled. He knew this place. "Was it all a dream?" he wondered for the hundredth time. He let his eyes roam across the endless prairie that ran like an emerald lake to the mountains, the slender blades of grass swaying back and forth with a lonely

sigh. Beyond the riverbank, the bluffs rose as high as three hundred feet.

The Hunkpapas arranged their lodges in the usual order, with Sitting Bull's tepee pitched at the southern edge, the door facing east where thick clusters of cottonwood trees lined the riverbank. Dakota found Sitting Bull leaning against the outside of his lodge with the sun warming his pensive face. With the blackbird perched on his shoulder, still showing no sign of wanting to fly away, Dakota slipped next to Sitting Bull.

Sitting Bull took his long pipe from its case, touched it to the ground, then pointed it toward the four directions. He filled and lit it and puffed long and hard, praying to Wakan Tanka after he exhaled a thick stream of smoke. Dakota took the pipe when Sitting Bull offered it to him and said, *"Pilamaya."* He drew the smoke slowly into his mouth, careful not to inhale for fear he would start coughing. The aroma of sumac leaves and dogwood settled pleasantly between them, as did a comfortable silence.

Many Horses emerged from the tepee wearing a light summer dress, her long hair spilling over her shoulders as she carried her twin brothers in either arm. She handed one of the boys to his father and the other to Dakota. When she bent close to Dakota he felt the warmth of her nearness. They smiled shyly at one another, then she was gone.

Dakota wondered which twin he held, Run-Away-From or Crow Foot. The baby felt warm and soft in his

arms. His skin was as dark as a buffalo hide, as were his eyes. Dakota looked at the baby's brother. He was already drifting into sleep, curled securely in the crook of his father's strong arm rocking him gently.

A sadness fell upon Dakota, darkening everything. He knew that neither twin would live beyond his fifteenth birthday. Crow Foot would die by a round of bullets, as would his father, on a cold and dreary day in December, the Moon of Popping Trees. Dakota sighed. Once again he wondered why his own people treated the Indians so badly. Why couldn't they just leave them alone to wander across their hunting grounds and chase the buffalo?

The baby wiggled. Dakota looked down and smiled at the boy who stared wide-eyed at him. Lifting him close to his face he blew loudly against his velvety stomach. The blackbird lifted its head and sang shrilly, "Chirp-a-ree, chirp-a-ree." The baby's eyes widened as he watched the bird, a smile lifting the corners of his mouth.

When the sun set over the mountain peaks, igniting the sky with streaks of purple and pink, Sitting Bull asked his nephew One Bull, only twenty-one winters, to accompany him to a high bluff across the river, opposite the Cheyenne camp. Curious, Dakota followed closely behind. Sitting Bull stopped and regarded him with uncertainty. The chief wore the worries of all his people on his dark wrinkled face that

day. Dakota's eyes pleaded with Sitting Bull. He made the sign with his hands that he would not make a sound. Sitting Bull shrugged wearily and said, *"Hoppo."*

Dakota followed in the shadows of the two men, keeping a few paces behind them as they waded across the river, then climbed a steep bluff. On the flat surface of the hill Sitting Bull laid his offerings to Wakan Tanka, placing the buffalo skull so that it faced eastward. Around it he arranged a buffalo rug, a pipe, and bits of tobacco.

In a mournful voice, the Hunkpapa chief pleaded with Wakan Tanka to keep his people safe from the soldiers and any misfortunes they might bring with them. He asked Wakan Tanka to take pity on him and his people and offered his gifts before the sun, the moon, the earth, and the four winds.

As they left the lonely hill, Dakota shivered, drawing closer to Sitting Bull. This was the very hill where he and his mother had parted from one another, the day of his fifteenth birthday, and the anniversary of the Battle of the Little Bighorn.

The following morning the sun beat down on the plains more fiercely than it had the day before. As the afternoon sun settled upon the villagers, it carried with it a lazy mood that quieted the campsite. Even the dogs lay sprawled in brown heaps among the tepees, too tired to chase the wild turkeys that scampered along the riverbank.

Many of the warriors rested under the shade of a nearby tree, or slumbered wearily inside their tepees, the sides rolled up to let in the scanty breezes. The sparkling rush of the river drew many to its cool waters. Dakota was only one among hundreds who splashed and swam across the river that day.

When he grew tired of swimming, Dakota pulled himself out of the river and walked like one who is not sure where his feet should take him. He hesitated among the cottonwood trees, feeling the weight of too many worries crowding inside him. The stillness of the camp bothered him. He had a strong desire to run through the village and shout to the warriors to get ready, to warn them that the bluecoats were coming. Instead, he scanned the horizon, looking for clouds of dust or anything that moved. He saw nothing.

Driven by uneasiness, Dakota sent his moccasins flying across the distance that separated him from his lodge. When he neared Pizi's dwelling he came upon the war chief dozing underneath the shade of a tree, one of his powerful arms flung across his face like a shield. He stopped and stared at the warrior for a long time, not knowing what to do. When he thought of what Savannah had told him, he felt a stab of anguish in his gut. He had to do something to warn Pizi, to let him know that he had to watch out for Reno's scouts.

The rapid beat of hooves drew Dakota's attention to a young warrior who was racing through the village. A loud cry shattered the silence. "Soldiers are coming! Soldiers are coming!"

Pizi flew off the ground and bolted to his tepee,

leaving Dakota alone to ponder what he should do. In only seconds the war chief was outside again, fully armed with his bow and arrows and a hatchet secure in his belt.

Dakota dashed toward Pizi and grabbed him by the arm. "Don't leave!" he cried. Pizi narrowed his eyes and pushed him aside with such force that Dakota stumbled backward. The chief strode off in the direction of the pony herd with Dakota calling after him frantically. It was no use. It seemed as if the destination of Pizi were set in stone.

Dakota burst inside the tepee and was met with a startled cry from one of Pizi's wives. Her eyes widened in fear, then indignation. He raised his arms in defense, but she shooed him out of her lodge with sharp words.

Uncertainty held Dakota to the ground. He searched up and down the village, not sure which way to go. The Hunkpapa campsite was coming to life in only a matter of seconds. The battle had begun. From every direction, people were making a mad rush toward the pony herd, while others were scurrying back from the river.

Dakota ran to his lodge, hoping to find someone who could help him, but he found it in turmoil as well. The women were busy stuffing the parfleches and gathering up the buffalo rugs in the event they would have to flee the village. At the same time, Sitting Bull was grabbing everyone by the arm and leading them outside.

Dakota snatched his parfleche and bridle and

bolted out of the tepee. Anxious villagers were scattering everywhere, women and children screaming and calling desperately for each other, scaring even the dogs that got in their way. Making a dash for the pony herd, Dakota dodged people, dogs, and horses as he ran.

In a flash, he was mounted on Cahli and galloping back to Sitting Bull's lodge. He found the chief astride his gray charger, his mother, Her-Holy-Door, and his sister, Good Feathers, seated behind him. Sitting Bull took off at a furious speed toward the hills where the other warriors were taking the women and children.

Another cry echoed through the campsite, more agitated than the last one. "They are charging! They are charging!"

Dakota looked where the heralds pointed. The Ree scouts under Major Reno had already crossed Ash Creek and were breaking through the edge of the Hunkpapa village. The major and his troops were not far behind, forming columns of four as they galloped toward the village.

The people separated, making an opening for their chief and his nephew One Bull, as they returned from the hills. They joined their men in the stand-still shooting, some firing from their mounts, others from the ground, exchanging gunfire with the bluecoats, keeping Reno's men from breaking all the way through their village. Many of the Ree scouts slipped past the warriors and began shooting inside the tepees, then setting fire to them. Pandemonium spread as fast as the fires

that consumed the rawhide tepees and turned them to dust. The warriors rounded up the horses at random and gave them to whomever was closest. The rapid pop of gunfire spooked some of the horses, making it difficult to hold them down. Ponies and warriors began to fall like stones tossed to the wind.

Dakota slipped off his pony and ran back inside Sitting Bull's tepee. Everyone was gone. He breathed a sigh of relief, sure that Many Horses had made it safely to the hills. He dashed across the tepee and snatched up the drum with the blackbird inside and was back outside in a flash. He would find Peeshkoh and drag him to Pizi's lodge if necessary.

As soon as Dakota mounted Cahli, he heard a mournful cry from somewhere behind him. He swung his pony around and saw Toskala stumbling out of her tepee, her buffalo rug loose around her shoulders.

He was off his pony in seconds, his arms encircling the old woman, stirring her toward Cahli. Gunfire and smoke filled the air, causing them both to duck and flinch every few seconds.

Getting Toskala onto Cahli proved to be more difficult than Dakota expected. She was still weak and shaking from fear or fever or both. He finally got on his hands and knees so she could step onto his back and pull herself onto the pony. As soon as she was mounted, Dakota handed Toskala the drum and pulled himself up behind her.

A number of the Hunkpapas' tepees were crackling and hissing from the fires set by the Ree scouts. It was impossible to see through all the smoke and

horses. Dakota felt paralyzed, unable to make a decision. Pizi's family weighed heavily on his mind, as did the safety of Toskala.

Another horse bumped roughly against him. He drew the reins in and came face to face with a Ree scout, his lance raised high above his head. In a panic, Dakota swung the pony around, barely missing the end of the lance, which came crashing down on the backside of Cahli. The pony neighed loudly and bolted forward.

At the first sign of a clearing, Dakota got his bearings and headed straight for the hills. He rode with terror breathing over his shoulder, too frightened to look behind him. "Where was Tahca Luzahan?" He couldn't imagine why he would leave his mother unattended like that.

Dakota reached the hill where hundreds of women and children huddled together, their voices rising in shrieks as they watched the fighting below them. He slipped off Cahli and reached his hands up to Toskala, who practically fell into his arms. He half carried her to the edge of the circle of people and helped wrap her buffalo rug more securely around her.

Toskala was crying softly, her thin, wrinkled arms still wrapped tightly around the drum. He wished he could say something that would reassure her. "She is my great great great grandmother," he thought, marveling at the notion of helping someone from his past. On impulse, he leaned over and kissed Toskala on her

cheek, then dashed off to get Cahli and return to the Hunkpapa camp.

When Dakota neared Pizi's lodge, he reined his pony to a halt. Pizi stormed past him, not seeing him. Dakota felt his stomach turn over in waves. The eyes of Pizi blazed as hot as the steel bullets that rang overhead. The war chief mounted his horse and raised his hatchet high above his head, making a wailing sound that came from somewhere deep inside of him.

Dakota edged his way toward Pizi's lodge, each step escalating his fear. At the entrance he faltered, too terrified at what he might find inside. He closed his eyes and flung the rawhide flap open and stepped inside. When he opened his eyes, the scene nearly knocked him over. He fell against the wall, everything unfolding inside of him. Both of Pizi's wives and his three children lay on the floor, their bodies ripped apart by the exploding carbines of the Ree scouts.

He stumbled outside and rode away with his head reeling, barely hearing the gunfire popping all around him, or the trilling of the Indians, or the cries of the soldiers.

Dakota found a place to hide behind a thick cluster of trees near the river. Leaning wearily against a tree trunk, he watched in a stupor as the battle unfolded before him. All of his reading and the stories his mother had told him had in no way prepared him for this. Everywhere men were fighting with determination, even though their faces were shrouded in fear.

From a distance he found the short, stout figure

of Major Reno, standing resolutely among his men as he shouted orders above the roar of gunfire. He wore a dark blue uniform with a line of shiny gold buttons running down the front of his shirt. On his head, a straw hat stood out starkly among the swarm of fighting men in their military caps.

From every direction, the Sioux drove their horses toward the soldiers. An excited cry spread among them. Through the haze of smoke and confusion, the hooves of a gray horse pounded the earth, its rider leading a pack of three hundred warriors. Crazy Horse sat tall and sure on his mount, his lance high above his head as he cried, "It is a good day to die, my friends! *Hokahe!*"

Disorder broke loose among Reno's men, scattering them like frightened rabbits. Major Reno moved among them, shouting words of encouragement that seemed lost in all the confusion. His face showed a trace of fear and indecision. The Sioux were everywhere, probably more Indians than he had ever seen in his lifetime. "Surely he must be wondering where General Custer and his backup are," thought Dakota. "There is no bloody way his small battalion of two hundred is going to hold back all these Indians!"

Reno squatted behind a steep ridge to confer briefly with Bloody Knife, one of General Custer's Crow scouts. As he turned his attention to his retreating troops, a bullet shot through the side of Bloody Knife's head, spilling his blood and brains all over Reno's face. Startled, the major leaped to his feet and scrambled for his horse. He drove his mount as fast as

he could toward the timber, where half of his men were holed up against an avalanche of roaring Indians.

The Sioux and Cheyenne closed in on the bluecoats' right flank, pushing them closer and closer to the river. Dakota saw everything as if it were unfolding in a movie, running at fast speed: a dozen soldiers falling from their horses, hitting the ground in heavy thuds, some being knocked from their mounts by the butt of a rifle or a war club, others falling when the warriors shot their horses from underneath them. The Indians moved in quickly, their war cries resounding across the plains as they hacked at the bluecoats with their knives and hatchets, sending the blood of their enemies flowing.

Dakota swallowed hard, keeping his eyes on Reno, anxious to know what he would do next. In all the confusion many of the soldiers had lost their horses. Some were already trying to ford the river on foot. The warriors were on them in a matter of seconds, knocking them down with their war clubs and holding their heads under the water until their bodies were still.

The desperate cry of a bugle rang out. Major Reno shouted words to his men. It didn't appear that many had heard him through all the noise and confusion. Not all the soldiers followed their commander as he fled across the river.

The Indians perceived this retreat as an encouraging sign. They formed a circle from behind and charged against the retreating bluecoats, fighting bravely to save their village. The warriors yanked many bluecoats from their horses, sending them tumbling

into the icy waters of the Little Bighorn River. When the bluecoats raised their heads above the water, they were no match against the Indians at hand-to-hand combat.

Dakota saw a soldier, who appeared to be wounded, make it across the river on foot. At the edge of the river he tried several times to get his footing, but his wounds were too crippling and he slumped back down to the ground. One of his fellow troopers saw him struggling and extended one of his stirrups to him. The helpless bluecoat grabbed it with both hands, letting the horse drag him up the steep bluff, his stomach bouncing up and down on the rough ground.

"The soldier is so close to the edge now. Perhaps he will make it after all," Dakota thought. But half a dozen warriors closed in on him, firing their rifles from their waist, sending a spray of gunfire all around him. The soldier released his grip on the stirrup and fell face down at the edge of the knoll, buried in a cloud of dust.

Dakota got up and wiped his damp hands along the sides of his breechcloth, then stumbled from the timber to the edge of the Hunkpapa camp. Already, women and children were flocking to the riverbank, searching frantically for their warriors, some lying either dead or wounded on the very ground that was their village.

A mournful keening rose above the scattered gunfire. The women found many of their men, good husbands and fathers, face down in their own blood,

never to look with loving eyes upon them again. Dakota watched the Lakota women in a state of shock as they reacted in a way that was out of character. A rage must have burned inside them as sharp as the blades on their hatchets. With hearts turned to steel, they turned their anger upon the dead and wounded *wasicus*, slashing and hacking at their bodies as if they were mere firewood to fuel their anger.

Even the children vented their anger upon the unfortunate bluecoats who had not made it across the river. Despite the desperate cries and pleadings of the *wasicus*, the children sent their arrows deep into their flesh, filling the air with the dull thud of their weapons hitting their mark.

"More soldiers! More soldiers!" The alarming cries of the Cheyenne rang across the Hunkpapas' war-ravaged village. The warriors pointed to the other side of the village where the Cheyenne were camped, where many of the women and children had taken refuge. Many of the warriors abandoned the fight against Reno and raced to the greater threat that awaited them at the northern edge of the village.

Dakota followed Pizi, who guided his band along the path that lay between the village and the river. At the same time Crazy Horse sped through the center of the village, gathering more and more warriors as he went along.

Dakota scanned the bluffs to his right, trying to understand why Custer had separated his command into four divisions. When the battle broke out, the

battalions were too far apart to be of any help to one another, with too many miles of treacherous land separating them.

Dakota followed Pizi and his warriors to the Cheyenne camp, where Pizi brought his men to a halt near the edge of the river at a place that would one day be called Medicine Tail Coulee. There they awaited the arrival of Crazy Horse and his reinforcements.

Below them, a few Cheyenne warriors fired shots from behind the sagebrush at the two hundred soldiers that formed a line along the opposite side of the river. Most of the bluecoats were mounted on gray horses, while a few were on foot, firing randomly across the river at the warriors.

On the other side of Medicine Tail Coulee, half of Custer's troops were making slow progress up Deep Coulee. It appeared to Dakota that the soldiers were stalling, perhaps waiting for reinforcements. He wiped the sweat from his forehead, well aware that General Custer had gotten himself into an impossible situation. He knew from history that the general had sent a runner to Captain Frederick Benteen. He closed his eyes and imagined the captain clutching the piece of paper, reading the general's words: "Come on. Big Village. Be quick. Bring pacs."

But the general would have to wait. Eventually, Captain Benteen would come to a halt at the top of a hill where he would witness his friend, Major Reno, fleeing with his men up the bluffs on the other side of the river. The fate of the Seventh Cavalry would hang in the balance once the captain gave the order for his

men to head toward the disarray on the hill where Reno and his men were surrounded.

The sharp trilling of Crazy Horse and his men drew closer and closer, finally stopping when they reached the place where Pizi waited for them. Dakota watched as the two war chiefs passed words between themselves. He knew they were organizing a charge that would eventually surround the bluecoats and bring them to their knees.

Dakota saw Peeshkoh among the many that followed Crazy Horse. He waved his hands over his head, calling, "Peeshkoh!"

His friend swung his pony around and trotted over to Dakota.

"*Mitakola*, you are alive after all!" he said, his face flushed from the heat and excitement. "We were afraid you might have deserted us and joined the bluecoats." Peeshkoh grinned when he saw the startled look on Dakota's face.

"Not me, Peeshkoh," he replied, turning his eyes away from his friend.

"Where is your bow, your quiver?" asked Peeshkoh in a loud voice, his eyes not wavering from Dakota

"I'm not fighting this battle," he said, meeting the eyes of Peeshkoh with the same tenacity.

Peeshkoh scanned the bluffs across from him. "We must protect the women and children from these bloodthirsty bluecoats. It is a good day to die if your heart is not afraid."

Peeshkoh's words stung, but Dakota let them sit with him awhile. He realized that his home and way

of life were back in Roundup. No matter how much he admired the Lakota and their way of life, his father's blood ran inside him, as did Jon-Jay's.

When his anger had subsided, Dakota asked, "Where have you been all this time?"

A flush of pink brightened Peeshkoh's cheeks. He lowered his eyes to the bow that lay across his lap. "I have been helping Tatanka Iyotanka at the village," he said. "Many were needed to see after the women and children." He adjusted his quiver so that it hung more freely over his shoulder. "I am ready to fight now," he said with a vengeance.

Dakota's voice softened. He had been through so much with Peeshkoh that he was afraid for him. "I will be waiting to see that you make it back safely with many brave deeds to tell."

When Crazy Horse and Pizi finished talking, the warriors divided like a flock of geese, splitting into two equal halves that formed a "V" across the river. Crazy Horse blew his bone whistle long and hard, letting even the bluecoats know that he was coming.

Pizi crossed the river where Medicine Tail Coulee joined on the other side. War cries rang across the bluffs, sending shivers of dread through Dakota when he saw the face of unbridled fury on Pizi, who would kill any bluecoat that got in his path. Without his family, Dakota knew, Pizi's life meant nothing to him.

The soldiers on gray horses continued to fire across the river at the approaching warriors. To the right of Pizi, the Cheyenne raised their war cries to an ear-shattering pitch and charged across the river. The

Plains Indians were united, strong in their medicine, strong in their determination to keep their village safe.

Dakota followed at a safe distance, fighting back tears of frustration. The warriors drove their mounts hard, making a wide sweep around the bluecoats. The soldiers at the riverbank saw the Indians coming from all directions. They scrambled onto their horses and began their retreat to higher ground.

The second group of soldiers kept pushing its way up the ravine, also trying to get to higher ground. It seemed as if all were determined to reach the middle knoll where they could reunite and make a stand.

A heavy volley of gunfire ripped through the skies, sending with it the smell of burnt smoke and fresh blood. Crazy Horse led a charge right through the middle of the soldiers, sending some scrambling for the river. Dakota saw their terrified faces, like cornered animals with nowhere to run. He knew they stood no chance against the united Indians. The soldiers had been led into a battle by a leader who was certain they would win. But who could have foreseen the countless number of Sitting Bull's followers?

The warriors ran the soldiers down, swinging their heavy clubs and hatchets over their heads, spilling the bluecoats' blood all over the valley.

Pizi and his warriors made a grand sweep from behind, joining the Oglalas to form a complete circle around Custer's men. While every fourth soldier held the horses, the other troopers shot their guns and rifles from the ground, but the warriors put an end to this kind of fighting, shooting many of the horses.

The mounts fell to the ground in heaps, only good now as shields to block the flying arrows and bullets that showered around the soldiers.

The circle grew smaller and smaller as the blue-coats bunched closer and closer together. At the center, Dakota was certain he saw General Custer, a tall, lean soldier with a mustache, wearing a fringed buck-skin shirt and dark pants. His golden hair slipped out of his hat as he fired shot after shot into the advancing warriors.

The warriors circled Custer's men like a pack of wolves closing in upon the wounded and dying. Many of the bluecoats threw their useless rifles to the ground in disgust after they kept jamming and locking.

Only a handful of men stood now. Dakota searched the face of General Custer. He stood defiantly against his adversary, letting his bullets rip into as many of the Indians as he could, before he too would fall. Between rounds of shots the general kept glancing furtively over his shoulder and scanning the distance to Medicine Tail Coulee, surely hoping beyond hope that he would catch sight of Captain Benteen and his men.

The general's face became a mask of steel, apparently hardened by the realization that all his dreams were dissolving into the dust that swirled around him and his men. Dakota reflected on Custer's burning desire to round up all the Indians and herd them back to their reservations at any cost. What a victory that would have been for him. How much better would be

his chances of running on the Democratic ticket for president of the United States.

The Sioux and Cheyenne made their final charge, dropping the last man. When the smoke and dust settled, the warriors fired their rifles and arrows at the ground, hitting anything that moved or made a sound.

One soldier bolted past the Indians and made it to a stray horse. He leaped onto it and flew eastward in the direction of the steep and jagged bluffs. He was well ahead of the four Cheyenne who pursued him, his horse sure and fast.

"He's going to make it!" Dakota thought. "Man-o-man-o-man! You've got to make it," he pleaded.

The Cheyenne began to slow down, realizing the bluecoat was too far ahead of them. At that moment the soldier stopped and looked behind him. He placed the gun to the side of his head and pulled the trigger. The blast echoed through the silence, the final death cry of the Seventh Cavalry. It was all over. The Indians looked around them. There was nothing more to shoot.

Dakota returned to the Hunkpapa camp, taking the same route between the river and the timber. Cahli shuffled along, his head low to the ground. Dakota was also slumped over, his face buried against his pony's neck. A noise behind the sagebrush brought him to full attention. He drew the reins in and listened. A soft, moaning sound came from the underbrush. He forced Cahli to a halt. Half hidden behind the brush was a

wounded soldier curled into a ball, three fellow troopers dead beside him. He was only a boy, no more than eighteen. His face was streaked with blood and tears. Between his sobs, he kept repeating, "Mother, help me, Mother." Then he fell forward and was silent.

Dakota slumped against Cahli, unable to lead her home. There was no sense to the fighting. Why did so many good men have to die in order to preserve their way of life? Dakota shivered when he thought how swiftly a person's life could change in the passing of an afternoon, never to be able to go back and settle all the misunderstandings that are forever piling up among the people you love. He thought of Pizi, who only yesterday had been swimming with his children in the same river Custer had tried to cross in the hope of capturing the village. Now Pizi's family was gone, as well as General Custer's: his brother, his sister's husband, his eighteen-year-old nephew—all dead on the very hill on which Sitting Bull had offered his gifts and prayers to Wakan Tanka.

Dakota continued along the path that led to the Hunkpapa circle, his thoughts engulfed in the gray clouds that carried him home, where his mother's arms held him tight.

CHAPTER 13

The Flight
of the Blackbird

After only a few hours of rest Dakota awakened to the shrill cries of lamenting from those mourning their dead warriors. Many Horses came to him with her horn bowl filled with water. He covered her hand with his own and brought the water to his parched lips. "How many times have Sitting Bull and Many Horses come to my rescue? What would I have done without them?" he mused.

Dakota noticed that Many Horses was different today. There was something in her eyes that spoke of grief and bewilderment. It was the kind of pain that would not go away easily. Dakota leaned forward and kissed her on her cheek. She smiled at him as he unraveled the string of beads and shells from around his neck and placed them over hers. "Will she wear them when I am gone?" he wondered. "Will she remember me?"

Many Horses spoke to him softly in words he didn't understand, but he sensed their meaning in the

inconsolable sadness of her tone. She was so close he could feel her breath on his face. He leaned closer and she surprised him with a kiss, a mere brush against his lips, followed by her girlish laugh. It was enough for Dakota to know at that moment that there would never be another girl who would make him feel the way she did.

Dakota left Sitting Bull's tepee with the blackbird perched on his shoulder. He let out a long sigh, feeling the ways of the Sioux pulling like a bowstring within him as he gazed upon the land, so profoundly beautiful and mysterious. From somewhere deep within him, Dakota had an inexplicable longing to embrace the earth, to stretch his arms along the ground and claim it as his own, to keep it always like this, unspoiled and untamed.

He drew a deep breath and forced himself onward, circling the Hunkpapa camp, viewing with hopelessness the remains of tepees that lay in piles of ashes, the smell of waste and squander heavy in the air. He knew this would mark the beginning of numerous and relentless attacks by the white men against the Plains Indians.

Dakota rounded up Cahli and the gray mare and trudged along the outside of the Hunkpapa village until he reached Toskala's tepee, still standing, though scorched by fire. He lingered for a moment, running his hand across the back of the gray mare. He had meant to give her to Sitting Bull, but a good horse would allow Toskala to trade for much needed supplies.

He called out to her in a tentative voice, thinking back to the day of their first encounter and his initial fear and distrust of her. But through it all she had kept him fed and clothed, and gradually she had allowed him to see a gentler side of her personality.

Toskala burst out of her tepee, looking like her old self—full of fire and energy. When she saw Dakota, her face softened and she said his name, stretching her arms out to him. Dakota let himself be smothered in her embrace, her heart beating fast against his ear.

Toskala called over her shoulder, *"Uwa!"*

A man emerged from Toskala's tepee. He was tall and powerful, with a face hardened by many battles and brave deeds. He listened patiently as Toskala spoke hurriedly, gesturing twice at Dakota.

Toskala took Dakota's hand and drew him closer to the man. Dakota drew his breath in like one experiencing both awe and disbelief.

The man raised his hand in greeting. *"Hau. Tahca Luzahan imkiyab,"* he said. Dakota felt the blood rush to his face. "I'm Dakota," he stammered, handing the reins of the gray mare to his great great grandfather.

Tahca Luzahan took the reins and nodded soberly at Dakota, a softness in his eyes that Dakota took for gratitude. Tahca Luzahan handed the reins to his mother and drew her into a close embrace. Dakota noticed the easy way they spoke to each other, the way Toskala smiled with pride at her son. Perhaps Peeshkoh was wrong about Tahca Luzahan. It was not easy to judge another person unless you saw the world from

their eyes, unless you stood side by side with them during the formidable events that shaped their lives.

The blackbird raised its head and chirped a high-spirited tune as Dakota waved good-bye to his past. The rewards of being a good relative, of being kind and dependable, settled within him until he felt warm inside. It was what Sitting Bull had wanted him to see with his heart, what his mother had insisted he see for himself.

Dakota found Peeshkoh sitting against the back of his tepee, sharpening his arrowheads.

"*Hau*," said Dakota, raising his hand in greeting.

"*Hau*," replied Peeshkoh.

Neither boy spoke for awhile. When Peeshkoh finally broke the silence, his voice sounded as if it were coming from far away. "We have lost our family, all of them. I have not seen Pizi since yesterday. He will never be the same."

"I know," Dakota whispered.

"Nothing good has come of this." Peeshkoh swept his hand in front of him, taking in the vast Little Bighorn Valley. "They will never leave us alone," he said bitterly. "More and more bluecoats will come and drive us farther and farther from our hunting grounds."

Dakota nodded, unable to express the pain he felt for all that Peeshkoh and Pizi had been through, what they would continue to go through in the years to come.

Peeshkoh rose suddenly. *"Hiyu wo,"* he said. "Let us go far into the mountains and find more elk."

Dakota shook his head wearily. "I can't. I have to go home now."

Peeshkoh regarded his friend with surprise. "Home? This is your home, *mitakola.*"

Dakota swallowed hard. "My mother," he began. He smiled, thinking of Savannah and how lost she would be without him. "I need to see her."

Peeshkoh flinched as if in pain. "You are a strange one," he said.

"I want you to have Cahli," Dakota said in a hurry, handing the lead rope to his friend. "You'll take good care of her, won't you?" He wanted to make sure that his friend understood how important the pony was to him.

"I will treat her better than my own—you know that," Peeshkoh said.

The two friends stared long and hard at each other, letting the silence say more than words. Dakota doubted he would ever again have a friend quite like Peeshkoh. He had learned so much from him, how to be strong and brave in the face of danger, and above all he had come to understand the value of friendship.

Dakota backed away slowly, raising his hand for the last time in farewell. *"Ake wancinyankin ktelo,"* he whispered to Peeshkoh.

Peeshkoh turned to go, then stopped. "You have found what you were looking for?"

Dakota nodded, the fire of enthusiasm bright within him. "I have found much more."

Peeshkoh strode toward him and gave his hand to Dakota, the two of them shaking in the way of the *wasicu* this time, in the spirit of friendship and loyalty. "Until I see you again," Peeshkoh said.

Dakota found Sitting Bull, his lance lying across his lap, at the hill where most of Reno's men were still holed up. He saw only despair on Sitting Bull's face. His people had gone against his warning to leave the bodies alone and not take their possessions. All around the Hunkpapa chief lay the white, naked bodies of the *wasicus*, stripped of everything they owned, mutilated beyond recognition. Dakota turned his face away, unable to understand how such terrible things could happen between people of different cultures, people who were for the most part good.

Sitting Bull looked down from his horse and studied Dakota, noticing the white man's clothes he was now wearing and the blackbird perched on his shoulder.

"*Tokiya la hwo?*" Sitting Bull asked.

Dakota pointed across the Little Bighorn River. "*Wagla*, home. *Mita ina*, my mother—." His voice broke. He didn't know how to tell Sitting Bull that he did not want to leave, that a part of him would never be the same once he crossed to the other side, but he had to go.

Sitting Bull reached his hand out to Dakota. "*Hiyu wo*," he said, helping Dakota onto his horse.

Dakota guided Sitting Bull along the river, searching for Medicine Tail Coulee. The blackbird chirped excitedly, then flew off in front of them, gliding low along a passageway that took them to the edge of the river.

Dakota pointed excitedly to a large black rock that stood alongside the river, the blackbird perched on top, trilling joyfully.

Tatanka Iyotanka and Dakota leaned against the rock. Sitting Bull took out his *cannupa* and began preparing the *cansasa* while he sang a prayer to Wakan Tanka. With the bowl of the pipe held in his left hand and the stem held toward his body, Sitting Bull carefully packed the smoking material into the pipe bowl. Sitting Bull and Dakota shared this sacred moment for the last time together. Dakota drew in the smoke, holding it deep inside as if it were a pleasant memory he wanted to savor. He turned to Sitting Bull and looked long into his *hunka's* eyes. *"Mita cante cantesica,* my heart is sad," he whispered.

Sitting Bull drew his arm around Dakota's shoulder. *"Aiii,"* he said, making a lonely sound that drifted across the river.

Dakota bit his lip. He didn't think he had the courage to leave.

Sitting Bull rose, ready to return to his people. He smiled at Dakota. *"Iyaya yo,"* he said gently.

Dakota understood that Sitting Bull was telling him it was time to go home. When he stood, the ground whirled beneath him. He grabbed Sitting Bull's arm to steady himself. Drawing a deep breath,

he stepped away from his *hunka*. "*Ake wancinyankin ktelo,*" he said, trying hard to smile.

Sitting Bull's face lit up, radiating an understanding of things beyond this world. With the confidence of one strong in his beliefs, he repeated the words, "*Ake wancinyankin ktelo,*" then turned his horse in the direction from which they had come.

Dakota watched him leave. His heart cried out to follow, but the pull of his old life called, drawing his gaze back to the Little Bighorn River. He sighed, realizing how much Sitting Bull had touched and altered his life. He had been more than an uncle to him—he had been his teacher and friend. "The sun in my soul," he thought, feeling the warmth of the man deep inside him.

Something weakened inside of him. For three weeks he had pushed his feelings back until they weighed like an anchor in the pit of his stomach. Now they rose to the surface, overtaking him with sorrow.

He slumped to the ground, his head falling into his hands. The pain he felt was not at all like the pain of the lance ripping through his shoulder, or the pain of the grizzly bear tearing open his flesh. This pain was far greater, sharper than anything he had ever known in his lifetime. It came with the knowledge of what lay ahead for Sitting Bull and his Hunkpapas, and all the other bands that made up the Plains Indians. It also came from the realization of how difficult it must have been for his mother, for all Indians brought up on the reservations, to adjust to a new way of life.

Dakota raised his head and gazed about, mar-

veling at the beauty of the land, the gentle stirring of nature. "This world will all vanish for them," he thought sadly. "This land that Sitting Bull loves."

Dakota rose, wiping the tears from his eyes, making his face hard. He looked down the path that Sitting Bull had taken. It was noticeably quiet, except for a sudden burst of song that came from a nearby cottonwood tree. He searched the branches in front of him until he spotted a meadowlark. It was singing a sweet, melancholy song that seemed to trail after the great Sioux chief.

As Dakota turned to face the Little Bighorn River, a curtain of darkness settled around him, as calm as half-sleep. Mesmerized, he watched the ripples sweep across the river and widen into swirling circles. A thin bar of light jetted across the darkening skies, followed by a crackling roar that seemed to split the sky apart.

Dakota leaned against the towering rock, frozen in a dreamlike state. The river widened and a spray of water streamed across his bare feet. "No!" he cried. He couldn't cross. Not now. It would be suicide.

The blackbird lifted its head and chirped shrilly. The past rushed inside Dakota in waves, swelling and ebbing. Many Horses, Toskala, Peeshkoh, Sitting Bull. . . .

An earth-shaking boom reverberated all around him, rocking the foundation and tearing it apart. The ground crumbled beneath his feet. Dakota's arms tightened around his bundle as he squeezed his eyes shut. A mighty force sucked him into the current. The past and the future merged as he reeled around the

whirlpool, body, heart, and soul, a billion particles spinning around and around.

A tunnel of light unfolded before him. By degrees the speed of motion slackened and his body drifted toward it, his thoughts fading into a blur. . . .

As Dakota came to, the noisy chatter of birds and the trickling flow of the river let him know that the world was still intact. Choking and sputtering, he gazed about. His chest was thrust against the riverbank, the lower half of his body submerged in water.

With little effort, he hoisted himself out of the river and scrambled to his feet. His first thought was of the blackbird. Frantically, he searched all around him. Nothing. Not a trace, not even a feather.

The name "Wahpa Tanka Newne" drifted inside him as he raced along the river, searching the edge of the bank and the span of water. When he had put a few miles behind him, Dakota stopped. The land was different, its very essence somehow altered. He no longer had the feeling of being in a land unspoiled. The sage and prairie were tinged with yellow, dry and parched under his feet. He remembered that summer had come early this year.

A cool breeze cut through his damp clothes and chilled him all over. Dakota drew another deep breath before he scurried up the steep incline. When he reached the top he spun around, giddy with joy. The

pavement of Battlefield Road twisted like a snake before him.

"I am home," he told himself with a lift in his voice. He sprinted forward at record speed, grateful for the quiet of the empty road. Not a soul anywhere, only the lonely grave markers of the Seventh Cavalry dotted the landscape on either side of him, their spirits urging him on.

At the end of the road, the Last Stand Monument towered above him. He stopped for a moment to scan the rows of the Seventh Cavalry names. He thought of the young boy he had watched die, his face streaked with tears, his comrades dead all around him. He knew that every name on that marble slab had a story to tell.

Dakota stiffened, his senses fully alert as a slight shuffling sound came from behind him.

"Dakota!"

He spun around. "Mom!" he cried. The relief at seeing her melted everything inside of him. He tried to speak, but his thoughts ran every which way. Instead, he seized her hands and squeezed them.

Savannah stepped back and examined her son from head to foot. She seemed to be at a loss for words as she beheld his wet and torn clothes, his bare feet and matted hair. "Whatever happened to you?" she asked, her expression conveying curiosity, rather than disapproval. "You look as if you've returned from an expedition, or something."

Dakota smiled at the irony of her words. "I have

been to the other side of the world and back again," he said, giving her a theatrical bow. In a more serious tone, he added, "I know what it is to be Lakota."

Dakota and Savannah fell silent, each regarding the other in a way that seemed to draw upon the past and all they had been through. His mother reached out and ran her finger along the "S" that marked his face. "You have a story to tell. I can see that." She smiled. "Are you ready to go home?"

Dakota nodded and slipped his arm through his mother's. "Wait until you see your garden. Jon-Jay and I have taken good care of it while you were gone."

Savannah drew her son in a tight embrace. "It's going to be all right this time."

Dakota heard the conviction in her voice and drew strength from it. "We'll make it work," he said.

As they were passing the lonely hill, Dakota stopped to regard the marker that indicated where General Custer had fallen. He slumped over the rail, his face tight and pinched as he replayed the battle scene in his mind, the circle growing smaller and smaller. He thought of Sitting Bull and his offerings to Wakan Tanka at the very place where the general and his men had fallen. Shaking his head, Dakota realized that this fateful day had changed all of their lives.

From above, the feathery swish of wings drew Dakota's attention to a trail of blackbirds as they skimmed across the red-streaked sky. From the end of the line, a single bird swooped down and circled four times in a wide loop over their heads.

Dakota's smile widened with the exultation that swelled inside of him.

"Man-o-man-o-man!" he cried, waving his arms over his head. "Wahpa Tanka Newne, you have found your way!"

The blackbird swept lower and hovered over their heads for only a moment. "Konk-la-ree," it chirped joyfully, as if proclaiming the world was, after all, rich in rewards.

GLOSSARY

Ake wancinyankin ktelo Farewell.
Akicita One who keeps order in the village.
Cahli Coal.
Cannupa Pipe.
Cansasa Red willow bark.
Hakicon Get dressed.
Han Yes.
Hau Hello. I am listening.
He mitawa It's mine.
Hiya No.
Hiyu wo Come on.
Hoka Badger.
Hokahe! A war cry.
Hoksila Boy.
Hoppo Let's go.
Hunka Chosen relative.
Imkiyab My name is. . . .
Inila Silence.
Inipi Sweat lodge ceremony.
Initi Sweat lodge structure.
Iyaya yo Go ahead.
Kola Friend.
Leta There.
Maka Earth.
Mihunka My chosen relative.
Mita cante cantesica My heart is sad.
Mita ina My mother.
Mitakola My friend.
Mitakuye oyasin We are all related.

Mni Water.

Nuwe unyinkte Let's go swimming.

Pilamaya Thank you.

Pte Buffalo.

Takuca? What?

Tatunkce Dung.

Tokiya la hwo? Where are you going?

Uwa Come (feminine).

Uwa yo Come (masculine).

Wagla Home.

Wakan Tanka Great Spirit.

Wasicu, wasicus White man, white men.

Waste Good.

We Blood.

Wicasa wakan Holy man or shaman.

Wicincala Young girl.

Wicokan Noon.

Wipazuka Waste Wi The Moon of the Chokecherries, June.

Witkotkoke Foolish.

Witko Crazy.

Wiyatke Cup.

Yahepa! Drink up!

BIBLIOGRAPHY

ANDERSON, GARY C. *Sitting Bull: The Paradox of Lakota Nationhood.* Harper Collins, 1996.

BERNOTAS, BOB. *Sitting Bull: Chief of the Sioux.* New York: Chelsea House, 1991.

BLEEKER, SONIA. *The Sioux Indians.* New York: William Morrow, 1962.

BRININSTOOL, E. A. *Troopers with Custer: Historic Incidents of the Battle of Little Bighorn.* Lincoln: University of Nebraska, 1952.

DIESSNER, DON. *There Are No Indians Left But Me! Sitting Bull's Story.* El Segundo, CA: Upton and Sons, 1993.

EWERS, JOHN C. *Indian Life on the Upper Missouri.* Norman: University of Oklahoma, 1968.

FIELDER, MILDRED. *Sioux Indian Leaders.* New York: Superior Publishing, 1975.

GRAY, JOHN S. *Custer's Last Campaign: Mitch Boyer and the Little Bighorn Reconstructed.* Lincoln: University of Nebraska, 1991.

HEDREN, PAUL L. *The Great War 1876–77.* Helena: Montana Historical Society, 1991.

MAILS, THOMAS E. *The Mystic Warriors of the Plains.* New York: Marlow & Company, 1995.

MCLAUGHLIN, JAMES. *My Friend the Indian.* Lincoln: University of Nebraska, 1989.

SANDOV, MARI. *Crazy Horse: The Strange Man of the Oglalas.* Lincoln: University of Nebraska, 1942.

South Dakota Department of History: *Report and Historical Collections*. South Dakota State Historical Society, Vol. XXIX: 1958.

TAYLOR, COLIN F. *The Plains Indians*. New York: Random House, 1994.

TILLETT, LESLIE. *Wind of the Buffalo Grass*. New York: Thomas Y. Crowell Company, 1976.

UTLEY, ROBERT M. *The Lance and the Shield: The Life and Times of Sitting Bull*. New York: Ballantine Books, 1993.

————. *Custer and the Great Controversy: Origin and Development of a Legend*. Lincoln: University of Nebraska, 1998.

VAUGHN, J. W. *With Crook at the Rosebud*. Lincoln: University of Nebraska Press, 1956.

VESTAL, STANLEY. *Warpath*. Lincoln: University of Nebraska Press, 1984.

WALKER, JAMES R. *Lakota Belief and Ritual*. Lincoln: University of Nebraska Press, 1980.

————. *Lakota Society*. Lincoln: University of Nebraska Press, 1982.

About the Author

A deep respect for the Plains Indians, and especially for Sitting Bull, inspired TERRY KRETZER-MALVEHY to write this book. In preparation, she traveled the route the Plains Indians took in June 1876, beginning at the Rosebud Valley where Sitting Bull's most famous sun dance occurred, across the Wolf Mountains and along Davis and Reno Creeks, and finally to the Little Bighorn Valley. Terry also visited numerous battlesites and museums, as well as the locale of Sitting Bull's birth and death near present-day Bullhead, South Dakota.

Terry lives in Auburn, California, with her husband, Roman, and daughter, Emilee. They spend their summers at their home in the Bitterroot Valley in Montana. This is Terry's first book for young readers.

OTHER TITLES FROM RISING MOON

The Last Warrior, by Suzanne Pierson Ellison
Best of Enemies, by Suzanne Pierson Ellison
Twilight Boy, by Tim Green
Walks in Beauty, by Hazel Krantz